CH00923193

Hopefully Ever After:
Breast Cancer, Life and Me

LINDA BARRETT

Cover art by KD Designs, Kim Van Meter

www.Alexandria2772@hotmail.com

Editing by Jerusha Rodgers

RabidBadgerEditing

E-book formatting by Web Crafters

www.webcraftersdesign.com

"The cancer experience can be a panic-fueled bullet train, but you meet some cool people in the bar car. In engaging girlfriend style, Linda Barrett's frank, funny memoir delivers an honest account of her difficult journey with just the right mix of love, friendship, wig-whipping and accessibly rendered science. Highly recommending for the newly diagnosed."

JONI RODGERS, NYT BESTSELLING AUTHOR OF
BALD IN THE LAND OF BIG HAIR

CHAPTER ONE

AND THEY LIVED HOPEFULLY EVER AFTER...

Tampa, Florida
Spring, 2012

A cancer diagnosis slams into you with the subtlety of a freight train. You can't talk or breathe. You stare at familiar surroundings, but everything looks distorted. *This isn't real*, you think. It's just an out-of-body experience, and it is *not* happening to you.

Except it is. Breast cancer happened to me twice, but you don't get any points for experience here. That freight train hit with the same ferocity the second time as it did the first.

After a decade of turbulence, however, I've now landed in a soft place. Outside the screened lanai where I'm sitting, a pair of sand hill cranes walks across the back yard, their bright red head-feathers in brilliant contrast with the soft gray of their bodies. They are tall and majestic birds, deliberate in their steps, their posture exuding the confidence I'm lacking.

"So much has happened since the first diagnosis," I say to my husband, who's nose-deep in a crossword puzzle. "I need to come up with the perfect starting point for this story."

Mike lowered the newspaper and looked at me over his reading glasses. "You do know you're always cranky when you begin a new book? But in the end, you always figure out what to do."

I must have looked doubtful because he glanced longingly at his paper before lifting his eyes to mine. "All right, all right. Here's an idea: try starting with our current lives. We're doing well. You're healthy again. We're finally living without holding our breaths. Begin in the here and now." With pen back in hand, he became engrossed once more in Across and Down.

Had I asked him to solve my problem?

No. I was just *kvetching* out loud. But Mike was being Mike, trying to find a solution. In our early days, long before cancer crept into our lives, I'd tease him about being my Knight in Shining Tinfoil. I'd expected him to share household chores and didn't want his head to swell because he shopped for groceries, cleaned the sink or vacuumed the carpets. Tinfoil seemed an appropriate garment.

More recently, when the going got rough, he was at my side—sure, steady and strong. A full-time job. I should replace his tinfoil with armor now, but I'm holding off. He knows it and laughs; we laugh together. Gentle teasing is our way. After more than four decades as husband and wife, we understand each other very well. I know why he suggested I focus this story in the present. He prefers to live in the moment, enjoying the sunshine and the sand hill cranes. He prefers to leave the dark days behind us. I can't blame him.

Although I'm half of the Linda-and-Michael team, I am also a mother, grandmother and novelist with fourteen works of fiction in print. My stories are about ordinary people in crisis, struggling to reach their happy endings. In 2001, when breast cancer hit me for the first time, I had to fight for my own happy ending, which I achieved and enjoyed for nine years.

Sitting on the screened porch today, I feel great, look pretty good and am planning for a long future. Part of me doesn't want to look back; I'm not that different from Mike. I should simply pack the cancer experience away in a mental trunk and, as we native New Yorkers say, *fuhggedaboudit!* The other part of me, however, wants to write about the turmoil and examine it for my own sake as well as for my children and grandchildren's sakes, and for those families facing the same situation. There was a specific reason for my cancers and something to be learned from them. Neither tumor was a random hit, but I didn't know that at the time.

On a sticky note taped to my computer is a quote I borrowed from Churchill: *Never, never, never give up.* Staring at those words got me through many a day.

Lab reports and medical records lay on the wrought iron table in front of me. Fact-checking is a must for any book. I need no notes, however, to recall my feelings as a two-time rider on the Breast Cancer Express. I need no cues to recall the complications the illness brought to my busy life and the heartache it brought to my family. And I need no reminders as to what I'd learned: in the fight to live, no decision is too extreme. They may be dramatic and scary, but if they work, so what? Twelve years have passed since my first bout with the disease, almost three years since my second one. Fortunately, that tumor wasn't a recurrence, but a brand new visitor. A good thing. Isn't it weird that a malignant tumor can bring good news? My last appointment with my surgeon at

Tampa General is long over, and I love my new oncologist at Moffitt Cancer Center who will monitor me from now on. Since our recent move to Florida, I've had to search for new cancer specialists, a chore I hadn't anticipated taking on while recuperating from a second bout of the disease.

The timing of our relocation couldn't have been worse. I adored my original oncologist who practiced in Houston, Texas, where I'd lived for sixteen years. I fought most of my cancer battles there and didn't plan on a second assault when we decided to move to Florida during the fall of 2010. I certainly wouldn't have left at that point had I known the future, but I didn't. Sometimes life presents choices, and we deal with the decisions we make.

Which brings me back to choosing this memoir's starting point. I briefly considered Mike's suggestion of Right Now. *Now* is important because it measures the time out from surgery: one year out, two years out, five years out. The more years, the better. *Now* is important because I am living in it. But, where's the story? I'm an author in search of a story, and my daily routines don't cut it. They're boring. As for the future? Well, that's the sticky one. *Tomorrow* doesn't come with a one hundred percent guarantee, so why think about it? Besides, tomorrow's events haven't happened yet, so where's the story?

The story lies in *Yesterday*. *Yesterday* provides the yardstick to measure the journey since the original diagnosis. I must sift through *Yesterday* in order to pull up remembrances and mine for the truth. For that is the meaning of memoir.

Sorry, honey.

CHAPTER TWO

ALLIES AND ENEMIES

Houston, Texas
February 2001

Tap. Tap. Tap.

My finger gently struck a spot on my right breast, and I heard the hard echo of a drum beat. The spot was left of center and low down toward the rib cage. I'd noticed it about six weeks earlier because it hurt when I slept on my stomach. So, I'd slept on my back or side and made believe it wasn't there.

This behavior is called denial.

A supposedly intelligent woman like me, however, can only live in denial for so long. I leaned over and woke my husband.

"Hey, honey. Touch this. Whaddyathink?" I put his hand on my breast, which usually made him very happy, and moved his index finger.

Tap. Tap. Tap.

"*What the hell...?*" He shot up and stared at me.

"I'm no doctor, but I don't like this."

My stomach plopped. Mike's always a straight shooter, and there's no one in this world I trusted more. After thirty-three years of marriage and raising three sons together, he'd proven himself time and again. In addition, his IQ is in the stratosphere, and that's a fact.

"Did you just find it or what?" he asked.

I shook my head and whispered, "Six weeks."

"SIX WEEKS? That's five weeks and six days too long."

"Well, I was hoping it would go away. It doesn't hurt much."

The next day, I was at my internist. "I feel a lump in my breast," is a magic phrase that can open a doctor's door at the last minute. In my case, I'd been a patient of Maya's for ten years. We were on a first-name basis by then, and I trusted her completely. After she examined my breasts, she tapped that area again, and said, "This spot has got to come out."

Had she said, *Out, out, damn spot?*

I was ready to joke, but Maya wasn't smiling, and I knew I was in trouble, the deep dark kind of trouble people don't want to face. People like me.

She referred me to an experienced surgeon who, I later discovered, was a sweet guy and long married himself. If I was still somewhat in denial, I now had a plan of action which not only illuminated reality but also removed some of my stress. I made the appointment, saw the surgeon and learned that the thingy in my breast couldn't be aspirated in the office. It was cut out the following Friday, a simple outpatient procedure under local anesthetic. The arrangement suited me just fine. I left knowing they'd call with the results of the biopsy in about two weeks.

"There's no reason to mention this to the kids yet," I said to Mike. "We don't even know for sure what we're dealing with, so why make them worry when I'm not even overly worried? After all, these things happen to women all the time." These things? A misdiagnosis? Much ado about nothing? A mom's job is to protect her children and not cause them undo anxiety. Mike thought about it for a moment and agreed. With no lab results, there was nothing to tell our three sons—young men focused on their careers, one on the verge of marriage.

Some people would have worried about the pathology outcome twenty-four/seven, but I forgot all about the lab work in the time that followed. After all, I'd done my part by showing up for the procedure, and now the medical people had to do theirs. Besides, I had a very busy life, busy enough to provide lots of distractions.

Do you ever wonder why everything happens at once? I'm talking about big events, not the everyday stuff. Is it mere coincidence? Karma? Revenge?

Three months prior to my medical issue, I'd accepted a challenging new job teaching the GED prep class at a nonprofit agency serving the homeless population. The program was headed by a woman I'd known in my last place of employment, a person who I liked and admired professionally. I applied for the teaching position partly because I trusted her. My instincts proved perfect. Kate and I worked together seamlessly and, in a short time, became fast friends.

On my very first day at this new position, I walked into the classroom to find thirty-five students who'd been without an instructor for two months. They were sitting and chatting, sometimes trying to help each other with the curriculum. Thirsty for a teacher and excited to see me, they wanted to start lessons *now*. My work was cut out for me—thirty-five students on different reading and math levels—but I was unfazed. Have I mentioned my love of goals and challenges, especially ones I believe in? I do believe in striving for an education. As I told my students, "Once you earn that diploma, no one but no one can take it away. It's yours forever. It might open doors to a career you've never thought of before."

I'd discovered this truth myself. I hold two degrees in Elementary Education from Hunter College, CUNY, and started my career in the NYC school system teaching third and fourth grade. After moving to Massachusetts with Mike and my then three-year-old first born, I became involved with Adult Education programs for the disadvantaged—high school dropouts, laid-off workers, cash and food stamp recipients—who were looking for a chance to turn their lives around. I loved working with adults and never returned to the grammar school classroom. My Master's degree opened an unexpected door. I functioned as "principal" of the program, serving hundreds of students annually in academic, job training, and job placement programs.

In Houston, I found similar positions, and was so involved planning for my new students that I forgot about everything else. Everything. Until a Friday evening in late February 2001 when I pulled into my driveway and saw Mike pacing while on the lookout for me. He waved a piece of paper. I parked in the garage and ran to him.

"What's the matter? What?"

His tears frightened me.

"The doctor called."

"Doctor? Doctor? What doc...tor?" Uh-oh. *That* doctor.

And I knew.

First, You Cry. Betty Rollins had been spot-on years ago when she'd titled her book about her mother's breast cancer.

Second, you visit the bathroom with the ultimate of diarrhea attacks. Fortunately, we had more than one bathroom. In the next thirty minutes, Mike and I were in and out of them like yo-yo's in syncopated rhythm.

Third, you fight. And never look back.

I forgave us our initial flight response to the bathrooms. I had to, or I'd be stuck in reverse instead of shifting forward. *Breast Cancer vs. Linda*. I was going to war and immediately pictured an army of knights, swords in hand, leaning forward on their well-trained steeds. I'd read a lot of historical fiction with descriptions of battles so vivid, the plains of war were easy to imagine. Those knights didn't know if they'd be dead or alive at day's end, or if they'd be prisoners or free men. The honorable ones either rode out each morning with courage and fought like hell or rode out with queasy stomachs but fought like hell anyway.

"We have allies and we have enemies," I said to my own Knight in Shining Tinfoil that Friday evening. "But our allies are numerous while the enemies number only two: Cancer and Fear."

Mike stared at me and waited, because sometimes he knows when to keep quiet. My heart pounded, my nerve endings sizzled like firecracker fuses. Who was that woman dancing a grotesque tarantella in the kitchen? I'd disappeared into in my own crazy world— or was channeling Scarlett's.

"I'm going to beat this," I yelled, waving my arms at the ceiling. "I promise you. As God is my witness, I'm going to beat this son-of-a-bitch. I will win, and we will go on with our lives." Grabbing a blue folder, the kind with pockets inside, I wrote, *The Cancer Gone Project*.

"Uh…Lin?" I glanced at Mike, my patient audience of one. "There's more. You need to know something else."

I shrugged. After the initial news, what else could there be?

"The surgeon didn't get clean margins when he did

the biopsy."

What did that mean? "So?"

"So, you need another surgery to get rid of any left-over cells."

And that's when I learned that for every step forward detours lurked in the dark. After the first explosion, the path to recovery remains strewn with landmines, waiting to trip the innocent.

"We also need to find an oncologist," continued Mike.

Oncologist. I shivered as words swam in my brain. *Oncology. Chemotherapy. Nausea. Radiation.*That was the short list. I pictured all the bald heads I'd seen in stories or television ads. I could be facing the same and a whole lot more. Chemistry had been my worst subject in high school, and now I'd have to learn an entirely new bio-chem curriculum with its own vocabulary. We all have our strengths and weaknesses, but truly, this would be a big challenge for me. So, in Scarlett style, I stopped thinking about it for the moment and vowed to worry about the science part after I found an oncologist.

"Call the Coopers," I said, referring to our neighbors around the corner. "Rose liked her doctor." Rose had had a mastectomy six months earlier and both she and her husband had sung the praises of her physician—his patience, upbeat attitude, and ability to explain everything. A sweet-natured woman, Rose had seemed so accepting of her fate, so accepting of all the procedures she'd undergone when Mike and I had visited with her at the hospital. While there, I'd tried to be encouraging, chatting and smiling, but in the back of my mind, I kept thinking, "Poor girl. Poor girl." I sure couldn't have guessed that a short time later, that "poor girl" would be me. Rose's sweet nature and attitude suited her. As for me? Not my style. I was definitely not a Rose.

"I'll call the Coopers," said Mike. "And then we have to tell the boys."

My stomach knotted tighter than a tangled fishing line. "And my mom," I whispered. "Oh, God. How am I going to tell her?"

A good daughter does not cause more pain to a wonderful mother, an eighty-four-year-old widow of a loving husband, living seventeen hundred miles away in New York City, and who's dealing with severe rheumatoid arthritis. A good daughter shields a caring mother as much as possible.

I started pacing, formulating a plan for Mom. "We'll call my sister first," I said. "Give Judy a day to digest the information, then she can be with Mom when I speak to her." Fortunately, Judy lived only twenty minutes away from our mother.

Perhaps I could have hidden the disease from Mom altogether considering the geographical distance between us. I gave it some thought and dismissed the idea. A secret would have been possible only if my illness required a short-term recovery such as with an appendectomy. Cancer treatment, however, takes time. The side effects are visible. More important, the close relationship between my mom and me had always been based on respect, truth and love. Lots of love. I couldn't, and wouldn't, treat her like a child. But...*oy*. I dreaded telling her.

"Let's wait until after I see the oncologist."

"Uh-huh."

"Because by then we'll have a cancer doctor and a treatment plan...and...and we'll be able to answer questions with real information." I paused, noticing my use of the plural subject pronoun. Michael wasn't the sick one, but I guess he was so much a part of me that "we" came naturally. We were in this thing together. For better or worse.

CHAPTER THREE

MY OVERNIGHT SUCCESS

Murphy's Law on steroids described my life in 2001. The timing of the diagnosis was terrible, although I suppose there's no "good" time to draw the cancer card from the deck. Not only had I just started that brand new teaching job, but something else—*something huge*—also happened at the exact same time as my first surgery.

In February 2001, my debut novel, *Love, Money and Amanda Shaw*, was released by Harlequin Books. Have I mentioned that this was a *very big deal* for me? And I'm not referring to money. After twenty years of pounding an IBM Selectric, then a Panasonic Word Processor, and finally a personal computer, I had hit my mark. Most folks I spoke with after the book came out, however, thought I was an overnight success! Most people, that is, except Mike, who knew exactly how much time I'd put into this "hobby," squeezing in the work at night, putting in fourteen hour days on weekends—all of this tucked in around the edges of my "normal" life.

When my *editor*—a magical phrase to me—called nine months earlier in May 2000, with the offer to buy the manuscript, we all agreed, including Mike, that my writing was much more than a hobby, and certainly more than therapy—an explanation some people used to understand this time consuming, non-paying activity. Dare I say, *I told you so!* when *Amanda Shaw* could be found at Barnes & Noble, Borders (R.I.P.), Books-a-Million, Wal*Mart, Target—almost anywhere books were sold?

My personal author copies arrived at the house in January, my last month of innocence and a month before the books hit the stores. I cried when I saw my name printed on the covers—the beautiful covers—where the artist had truly brought the winter ski slope setting to life. Awestruck. I was totally awestruck. After being blessed with three precious sons, I had once more given birth. And this kid wouldn't talk back!

When Mike saw the books, he stroked the covers, his fingers pausing on my name. He looked at me, and I saw his lips move. Couldn't hear the words, though. My guy had choked up—a rare moment when I wished I'd had a camera. But after ten seconds of amazement, we were twirling around the kitchen, our arms and legs intertwined as we celebrated.

I'd labored over this first story, creating characters and conflict, writing dialogue, revising scenes and learning from my editor. A labor of love that took about nine months. Publication of my novel was the payoff after years of writing poems, essays, short stories and family memoirs. Publication was the payoff after attending numerous writing workshops and auditing creative writing courses at a local college. It was the payoff after investing in a library of reference books—and studying them—on the craft of fiction. Full disclosure here: *Love, Money and Amanda Shaw* was not my first attempt at a novel; it was preceded by several forgettable stories that currently reside on a closet shelf. But my investment of time and money had finally resulted in a published novel. My apprenticeship had led me to my goal.

Overnight success stories are rare in publishing. The truth is that writing a novel is hard work. It's about weaving numerous threads until they're blended without a trace of seams. Unlike the romantic image of a writer banging out a story at the keyboard, the words don't often flow like water over Niagara Falls. No one supplies you with peeled grapes either. There is no paycheck while you're in the wannabe mode. I didn't care about any of that. I just wanted to tell my stories and hoped people would want to read them.

When *Amanda Shaw* was published, I was also under contract for a second book. My fledgling second career seemed to be growing, and my spirits soared at the opportunity. I knew how lucky I was, how determined I'd been and how tough the competition was for actual contracts. I'd been told that ten thousand manuscripts had hit my publisher's slush pile in 1999, the year I submitted *Amanda Shaw*. The editors pursued only one hundred. And of those, not every story made it to publication. Given the odds, I'd vowed to protect this opportunity at all costs. What I didn't know was how quickly I'd be tested.

After a month of celebrating the launch of this much-desired second career, I got hit with the breast cancer diagnosis. Now talking the talk about my writing career wasn't enough. I'd also have to walk the walk—immediately. My test had begun. When the initial shock of the diagnosis faded, I figured out my strategy: *Don't tell, don't tell, don't tell.*

I'd always thought of myself as an upbeat, friendly gal with a conversational bent. I discovered I could also keep my mouth shut. My cancer was a secret I kept from my editors, a fairly easy accomplishment when most business was conducted through the U.S. Mail or FedEx. Terrified of gossip, I also kept the secret from my local writing group. Strongly reinforcing my decision to maintain secrecy were four multi-published author-friends in whom I'd confided. They quickly sent me a floral bouquet with a note that read: We're plotting a *Happily Ever After for you.* I smiled, I cried, I was comfortable with my decision. And I still have their card.

CHAPTER FOUR

THE FACTS, PLEASE, JUST THE FACTS

At the beginning of March, I met again with the surgeon to discuss my options. I had two: 1) a mastectomy, and 2) cutting breast tissue until the margins were clear—in other words, enlarging the lumpectomy. Visually at this point, I had no indentation, and other than a scar, both breasts looked almost the same.

Of course, I asked him the age-old question: if I were your wife, what would you recommend? And without hesitation, he said, "a mastectomy." I agreed with him. I wanted a once-and-done procedure, getting rid of every possible cancer cell. Dr. Joe explained that I had to confirm this decision so he could prepare the operating room appropriately since the two procedures required a different set-up. I left his office mumbling, "Take the damn thing off."

Later that week, I met my oncologist for the first

time. Rose's doctor. Rose, who believed Dr. Eric Bernicker could have created the world in seven days if he'd wanted to. To my delight, I knew I was in good hands five minutes after meeting him. How else could you feel with a physician who sits back and listens? Who *never* glances at his watch? And who wears an orange polka-dotted bowtie? I walked in, saw his neckwear and grinned. The guy really had me at hello.

During the next hour—a full hour or more—I learned the detailed results of my pathology report. We reviewed the choices I had regarding the next surgery and the possible outcomes for each decision. Dr. Bernicker spoke in language that even I could understand.

Surgical report: Tumor size: 1.5 cm, which put it in the Stage I category—good news. Tumor type: Invasive Ductal Carcinoma, Grade 3 with a total histologic grade of 9—bad news. That high score indicated a very aggressive tumor. But not to worry. The next surgery—be it a lumpectomy *or* mastectomy would excise all the affected tissue.

"Whoa! Wait." Lumpectomy *or* mastectomy? A choice. "Let's talk some more about a mastectomy."

I had just about made up my mind to go the mastectomy route. But Dr. Bernicker started talking about "breast conservation." If there was sufficient breast tissue remaining after the surgeon obtained clean margins, I could choose to keep my breast. In either case, I'd need four rounds of chemo. No getting around that. But a mastectomy would avoid radiation—a good thing. On the other hand, the entire breast would be gone, including the magic nipple button. One less erogenous zone—a bad thing.

And it was *my* choice to make. Wouldn't you know it? The biggest decision in this entire muddle was up to me, the least medically qualified person on the whole team. As for Mike – well, he said he'd love me either way, and this decision was totally mine. I had the weekend to think it over. Three days. Dr. Joe, the surgeon, needed to know on Monday.

Statistics. I needed to compare survival statistics. Dr. Bernicker assured me the survival rate in my case was exactly the same with either procedure—about 96%. He quoted the most recent studies and said that in the end, it really came down to being a psychological choice. What could I live with?

If I got rid of the breast, I'd be getting rid of something that could have killed me. Phantoms of a repeat performance might be diminished. Every woman with breast cancer worries about the "what ifs…?" I was no exception. "What if it happens again because I didn't choose a mastectomy?" Once again, I thought I should just get rid of the breast and be done with it.

On the other hand, a mastectomy is forever. Once that surgery is performed, I couldn't change my mind. How would I feel glancing at myself in the mirror every day and seeing only a scarred flat chest on one side? A reminder of what happened. Would I be more comfortable preserving my breast even though part of it would be missing and the shape would be different? Would I be taking an avoidable risk?

A choice: breast or no breast.

And there was more. During the surgery, we'd also examine my lymph nodes. We'd find out if the cancer had traveled to the sentinel node, the one closest to the breast. If so, then Dr. Joe would remove it and examine the second node and third and remove them until he reached a clean one. Best-case scenario: no lymph node involvement at all.

In addition, I'd be getting a portacath. Dr. Joe would insert a special catheter into my chest cavity near my shoulder. The catheter would be used to facilitate the chemo infusions.

Question: How much information could I absorb in that first visit?

Answer: As much as I had to. Nothing beats motivation to take on the unfamiliar. Suddenly, I became a science student.

My surgeon would be very busy next week—breast, lymph nodes, catheter placement, and I still had a decision to make, and a dinner to share with a Harlequin editor, before then. In fact, the dinner was set for the night after that first appointment with Dr. Bernicker.

What horrible timing. One of the Harlequin editors was coming to town for a conference, and I had committed to having dinner with her and one other author. Two other writers had conflicts that night, so I couldn't back out. Believe me, I wanted to. I wanted to stay home, do statistical research of my own, and then crawl under the covers. I'll never know how I managed to put on my big girl panties and get through that meal, that never-ending meal.

I remember sitting at the dinner table, making conversation. I remember the restaurant because we had white-glove French service, so different from the service in my usual haunts. But mostly, I remember thinking about the pros and cons between mastectomy and lumpectomy.

As I sat there, playing with the chicken and rice, barely able to swallow a bite, barely able to down a sip of water, the front and back of my mind were in two different places. I knew my mouth opened and closed; I knew words came out. Somehow I kept up with the conversation while my thoughts were definitely elsewhere. I'm happy to report, however, that in the end, I pulled off that dinner like a Broadway star. Or perhaps I was the heroine in my own novel with enough motivation to reach her goal: Protect the career. *Don't tell.*

Innocent editors had become the enemy instead of the allies I'd been looking forward to working with. A damn shame, and I hated myself for it. But I couldn't trust them—didn't know the business well enough—and thought I had no choice.

The next day, Saturday, I was alone in the house, making a comparison list at the kitchen table. My two doctors had differing opinions about the surgery. Since speaking to them, I'd researched survival rate statistics through several people close to me, *allies* who had my back.

My cousin, Dr. Barbara Edelman, a research statistician in the health care outcomes field with a professional network, had confirmed what my friend, Dr. Mel Pratter, Professor of Medicine, had told me: survival rates in cases like mine were statistically identical in the two procedures. Independently, each one confirmed Dr. Bernicker's statement. Since I thought both these wonderful people were brilliant and, more important, cared about me, I had great faith in their information. Barbara had put out calls to her colleagues who were keeping stats on breast cancer in long-term studies. One study was of two thousand women over a twenty-year period from Worcester, MA, where I had lived for twenty-three years! Half these women had chosen mastectomy and half had preserved their breasts. The ten-year survival rate was 99% in both groups. I started to rethink my initial response to Dr. Joe.

When Mike returned home that day, he took one look at me and said, "You've made your decision, haven't you?"

I nodded. "Let's write up the instructions."

****

26

This is the written directive I gave to Dr. Joe, which I subsequently saved in the blue *Cancer Gone Project* folder:

TO: Dr. Joe
FROM: Linda Barrett
DATE: March 19, 2001
RE:Course of Surgery on Tuesday, March 20, 2001

After visiting with my oncologist, Dr. Bernicker, and investigating statistical outcomes through other sources, I have decided to **try to preserve the breast** if possible. To that end, I'd like to do the following:

1. Put in a portacath, but NOT a Hickman as per Dr. B.
2. Excise tissue around where the lump used to be, and through frozen sections, see whether we can get clean margins without removal of so much breast tissue that the breast is no longer meaningful. **If we can get clean margins and maintain sufficient breast tissue to conserve the breast, then DON'T do a mastectomy.**
3. Test lymph nodes. I understand that lymph node involvement should have no bearing on breast conservation.
4. My husband will be in the waiting room, or wherever else you tell him to be, and is available for consultation at any time.

Thank you very much. I know you'll do a great job. Make sure I wake up when it's over!

***

I opened my eyes, looked down, looked up. All I'd seen were bandages and a drain.

"What? What happened?"

"It's still there," said Mike, who immediately gave me a new nickname: *One-and-Seven-Eighths*. Honestly, that's what he called me at least once a day from then on. Where there had previously been only a scar, there was now a divot. Fortunately, it was on the underside of the breast and not visible. I could still wear all forms of necklines.

I left the hospital with a drain in the incision, which was removed two days later. From my perspective, the whole procedure had been a piece of cake. The frosting on top came the following week in Dr. B's office when he told me the result of the pathology report:

RIGHT SENTENEL LYMPH NODE – GROSSLY BENIGN.

I love the word benign. Clean. No cancer in the lymph system. The cancer had not traveled to the rest of my body. Of course I knew there could be a tiny chance that somehow one cell managed to escape, but I couldn't worry about one cell. I had to run with the statistics. Clean lymph nodes!

The relief made my limbs feel like Jell-O, and I sagged back in the chair. Was I lucky or what? I knew of the long term complications some women (up to 20%) had when most or all of their lymph nodes were removed, complications like fluid buildup and swelling in their arm, hand and chest wall. Fortunately, it's all treatable, but they must take precautionary measures to protect themselves for the rest of their lives. So I was ready to celebrate this victory. Heck, I'd celebrate every victory along the way, major or minor.

"Now let's talk about the hormone receptor status," said Dr. Bernicker.

Hormones. More biology. More science. I grabbed a pad of paper. I remembered that Rose took Tamoxifen and would continue to take it daily for five years in order to suppress her hormone production. I was ready to hear something similar. Instead, I heard the complete opposite. I had negative hormone receptors.

Here comes the science part: two-thirds of women with breast cancer are hormone receptor positive which means that estrogen and progesterone feed their tumors and make them grow—sort of like fertilizer on a plant. Hormones are produced by the ovaries and by body fat, which is why the breast cancer rate is higher in overweight women.

My tumor, however, was considered a triple negative type. It did not depend on estrogen or progesterone to grow. These hormones in my body had no effect whatsoever on this tumor. Also, my tumor was negative for the Her2/neu, a protein that promotes the growth of cancer cells. So, there's the triple—two hormones plus one protein.

Being negative is both good and bad. Had I been positive, I could have taken Tamoxifen for five years after my initial treatments were over. In 2001, Tamoxifen was the hormone suppressant of choice, the best one on the market, and is still one of the best. Although it could produce such side effects as vaginal dryness, hot flashes, mood swings and other menopausal type symptoms, as well as headaches, nausea and leg cramps, the drug did the job of preventing another tumor from forming in these HR+ patients. Some women tolerated the side effects very well; others did not. But basically, the statistics for non-reoccurrence were good because of Tamoxifen.

For patients like me with negative receptors, Tamoxifen was useless. The hormones I produced had no effect whatsoever on the tumor. The bright side: since the hormones weren't affecting *this* tumor, I didn't have to worry about them at all or take pills with potential side effects.

On the other hand, I also didn't have a five-year security blanket.

CHAPTER FIVE

SPREADING THE NEWS IS WORSE THAN HEARING IT

"Hi, Mom. How are you?"

Blanche was fine. Absolutely, positively fine. She said so!

Right. What's the definition of *fine* for an eighty-four-year-old, 115 pound woman with severe rheumatoid arthritis who needs a walker with a built-in seat for outdoor excursions, takes fourteen medicines daily and has a personal aide six hours a day? What does *fine* mean for a woman who holds onto the furniture inside her apartment in order to make her way from one room to another?

When my dad was alive, my mom wasn't as disabled, but he'd anticipate her needs even then, opening jars, doors, carrying groceries and driving her to work. Not that she needed the ride—New York City has excellent public transportation—but he wanted to provide it. His eyes shone with love whenever he looked at her. According to Mom, she and Dad had been an "item" before the war and remained so for the forty-four years of their marriage.

While growing up, I don't remember my mother ever wearing fashionable shoes. Instead, her closet shelf held boxes of orthopedic oxfords and sandals in every color. She never complained either about her discomfort or her unfashionable self. She tried to manage the disease by building muscle to support her joints. To this end, she followed along with Denise Austin's exercise tapes. Every single day. She went to aerobics classes, too, and did the best she could. She fought back with her own willpower, but seeing her in such agony always brought me to my knees.

"Mom, how can I help? I hate to see you in so much pain."

She'd wave her arm at me and reply, "It's not so bad, Linda, not so bad."

So, what do you call a woman who refused to give in no matter what? What do you call an elderly woman who still wanted to shield her adult daughter?

I'd call her remarkable.

"So, is Judy there with you...?" I asked. "Good, good. I know...it's Wednesday. She always stays overnight on Wednesdays."

I listened, glanced at Mike, took a deep breath.

"I need to tell you something, Mom. It's a little unsettling, but I'm going to be fine in the end. Absolutely fine. Are you sitting down?"

The words choked me. Somehow I told her. "It was small, a very small—like a dot—tumor. We took it out already and I'm clean, but it was...cancer. So now, I'm shopping for a wig."

"Oh, my...oh, my..."

"But you don't have to worry. The stats are great. I'm going to recover. And I'll be fine. Judy already knows everything...so you can talk more to her after I hang up."

But she wanted to speak with *me*. I gave her my start date for the chemo—April 19th—a Thursday. I'd return every three weeks until the four rounds were completed. "My doctor is fabulous, Mom, and he's got everything under control. Houston has the greatest medical facilities in the world." True enough, with M.D. Anderson Cancer Center as part of the medical complex.

In reality, my chemo would be administered in Dr. B's clinic, but I thought Mom—a New Yorker through and through—would feel better knowing that I wasn't living in a hick town, medically speaking.

After answering all her questions and hanging up, I handed the phone to Mike. "You call the boys and *your* mother. I can't do this four more times."

Calls to New York, Florida and Massachusetts. At this point in our lives, our sons had all graduated from college, had moved out and onward. The phone calls between us, however, remained constant. We'd raised good boys with loving hearts who wanted to believe the best, which was a big factor in having Mike call them. They knew he wouldn't lie. Whereas I...? I might sugarcoat the truth.

Of course, I spoke with them all, promised my sons I'd be absolutely *fine,* and because kids—even grown ones—want to believe in happily ever after, they hung up feeling relieved and went on with their busy lives, building careers, meeting girls, and remembering to call home.

Mike's mom is also my mom's third cousin. On the day I was born, Dee stopped off to visit at the hospital, so I can truthfully say, she's known me my entire life. She's always been terrified of cancer due to losing several siblings and a father to the disease, so she had to be handled particularly gently. When Mike broke the news, she began crying into the phone, begging God to give her the cancer instead. I spoke with her myself, reassuring her that I'd be *fine*. She needed to hear my voice, to know I still walked on God's green earth. I was lucky to be blessed with a wonderful mother, but to have a loving mother-in-law as well? You can't beat that combo.

CHAPTER SIX

INTRODUCING BETTY

Under other circumstances, shopping for a wig would have been a hoot. Fun. A good time. Under other circumstances, I would have tried on styles not my own, colors not my own and had a blast—like playing dress-up in my mom's clothes when I was a kid. Under these circumstances, however, I wanted a perfect match.

I bought Betty as soon as I tried her on. Shoulder length, medium blonde, almost exactly like my own style, but better. Impervious to the weather, she'd look good anywhere, anytime despite the intense Houston humidity. My natural waves couldn't handle Houston, so maybe there was an upside to this. Betty came with her own shampoo, conditioner, hairspray, comb, instruction booklet and lightweight head form where she'd spend the nights. We boxed her up, paid the lady and went to the car.

"It'll be like going out with two women," said Mike, getting behind the wheel. "I've got you *and* Betty. Hmm…This could be fun!"

I whacked him. Lots of fun.

My cancer-world became more of a reality every day. I realized that Dr. B was the driver of my bus and would be for the rest of my life. He had actually directed Dr. Joe about the surgery and determined my course of future radiation. As the medical doctor specializing in oncology, he was the hub around whom everyone else gathered. Cancer is an insidious beast; we'd keep it at bay, but be on the lookout forever after. I'd followed his instructions about the surgery, and now, I'd follow his advice about having the wig at hand before I actually needed it. Ergo, the shopping trip before my first infusion.

Dr. B's office was located fifteen minutes from where I worked. A lucky happenstance. His place is more than an "office." It has exam rooms, certainly, but also an infusion center where patients receive their chemo privately or semi-privately, a lab, a nurses' station, reception area and a waiting room. The clinic has grown since my first visit a decade ago, with a number of other physicians sharing the space now, but the atmosphere of privacy and calm still prevails. The extraordinarily talented and compassionate nurses remain a hallmark of his practice. They are preservers of sanity. Emotional lifesavers. I loved all of his RN's. Still do.

I started chemo on a Thursday in mid April. I taught class in the morning, and then went to the clinic. Sure, I was nervous that first time, but the nurses, well, they put me at ease. After drawing blood and testing it to assure normal counts, they used the portacath Dr. Joe had inserted beneath my shoulder to connect me to the chemo IV. I barely felt a thing. Really. The procedure was virtually painless.

"So, what cocktail am I getting?"

"The Cadillac of chemo," Dr. Bernicker said.

"Adriamycin."

I had read about the Red Devil, named for its color and side effects, the main ones being nausea/vomiting, mouth sores, hair loss and fatigue—Adriamycin was the "go to" drug, the drug of choice among cancer specialists. It works by slowing or stopping the growth of cancer cells. I'd also get Cytoxan mixed in with it. Cytoxan blocks the copying of cancer's DNA from one cell to the other, interfering with its growth. Together, the A-C team does a heck of a job. It works! It's been proven. And that's what I reminded myself three days later as the nausea made itself known.

The problem for patients is in how the chemo cocktail works. It not only kills the fast growing cancer cells, it kills all fast growing cells in the body—including the healthy ones. Hair follicles, cells that line the digestive tract, and blood cells are all rapidly dividing cells and are interrupted by the drugs. This is why cancer patients lose their hair, become nauseous and have tricky blood counts, which could affect their immunity.

I didn't vomit, but on Sunday, when the nausea really kicked in, I moaned and groaned, waiting for it to pass. Silly me. It stuck around all day. I'd been told that the third day post chemo could be the roughest, which is why we'd chosen Thursdays as my infusion day. Being nauseous at home on a Sunday would certainly be simpler than trying to teach class. The plan worked. By Monday morning I was human enough to participate in life again.

Dr. Bernicker had referred to Adria as the Cadillac of chemo, the top of the line. With all its advantages, it had one disadvantage, and it was a big one. Adria could be used only once in a lifetime. It had a tendency to damage or affect the heart, and people with heart conditions could not take this drug. Fortunately, I wasn't in that group, but…

"But what if I get cancer again?" And why do I always think the worst?

"We've got other fine drugs that will do the job," Dr. B said. "Let me worry about that."

Sure. Okay. I had other things to worry about, too, and I'd be headed for a meltdown if I took on more. But the question lingered in the back of my mind for a long time. I've been called a worrier many times in my life and never liked the description. But now I was beginning to see what others saw in me.

The office visit took about three hours including the blood work, infusion and the very important Procrit injection afterwards. Procrit is a drug that causes bone marrow to produce more red blood cells to compensate for the chemo's destruction of them. I'd be getting a Procrit shot after each chemo treatment as well as during my weekly blood-test visits, if needed. As it turned out, they were needed. My red blood counts were often low.

Not too bad, I thought as I drove home after that first treatment. I was starving for lunch and stopped off to get a quick burger. Hey, maybe I'd escape all those awful side effects. Of course, Sunday hadn't come around yet.

My wishful thinking, however, kept my spirits up— a good idea, because the phone never stopped ringing that evening. My sons, mom, friends—all wanting to know about the first treatment. Finally, I was able to share good news.

"Not to worry," I told them. "It was great. I'm *fine*. Everything will be fine."

That night, I emailed my four published friends: *One down, three to go. I'm doing fine.*

If I ever had to choose one handy-dandy, cover-all-bases word in the English language, *fine* would get my vote.

CHAPTER SEVEN

MIKE AND THE HAIRCUT; BETTY'S DEBUT

Lady Godiva. Rapunzel. Cleopatra. The young wife in the Gift of the *Magi* who sold her tresses in order to buy her husband a fob for his watch. In true O. Henry style, the husband sold his watch to buy combs for his wife. So, what did all these ladies have in common?

Hair! Beautiful, long, thick, shiny locks. Every woman's crowning glory. I looked in the mirror a week after my first treatment and stared at my waves. Not the thickest, not the most beautiful, but in general, I liked what I saw. I was used to my mop. I usually knew how to manage it—except when the humidity had the last word.

In his office, Dr. B had cautioned, "Don't wait until your hair falls out, and you find it on your pillow, in your car, on the floor. Cut it yourself. Then use an electric razor. Start wearing the wig before you actually need it."

His advice rang in my ears as I studied my reflection. He'd told me I'd lose my hair exactly two weeks after my infusion—give or take a day or so. One week down, one week to go. I tugged a lock. Ouch! Still there. Still felt strong. I pulled at the other side and got the same result.

Yeah, I knew it was only one week since the treatment, but maybe…was it possible that I could be an exception to the hair loss rule? I had a cousin treated for breast cancer who didn't lose all her hair; it just got a bit thinner. I could live with that. Of course, I didn't know which drugs she'd received; maybe she hadn't gotten Adriamycin.

I touched the scissors that lay on the counter, grabbed a chunk of hair, lifted the scissors, then put them down. Maybe I'd wait another day…or two, or…

Five days later, on Sunday, I woke up to find strands of hair on my pillow and in my bed. When I touched my head, narrow clumps clung to my fingers. A huge knot formed in my stomach. I leaned over a trash pail and kept pulling out hair.

"No, no, no," said Mike, coming into the room at my call. "I've got a better idea."

He led me onto the back patio. I plopped into a chair while he went inside the house. Little sobs kept escaping. Was it vanity? Or was it another reality check? Yes, I had breast cancer. I really did, despite exercising, keeping a good weight, and eating healthily. I couldn't pretend it away, although I still wondered why I'd been hit in the first place. The air? Water? Food? Or just a random act of cancer?

Mike returned with a brush, scissors and electric razor. "Whoops, looks like I forgot the tissues." Back and forth he went again.

I grabbed a bunch of Kleenex and blew my nose. "Okay, you Southpaw. Can I trust you to use that razor?"

My knight always had good intentions, but fine motor coordination was a skill he had yet to acquire, and I had little hope.

"I wouldn't hurt you for the world."

"I know, not on purpose…"

"I'll go very slowly."

I straddled the chair, presenting Mike with my back, covered my face with tissues and let him at it.

Slowly, slowly, he cut one hank at a time all around my head. He'd brought a mirror, but I didn't want to look. Instead, I touched. Short, thin. Sometimes smooth skin. Scalp.

Then I heard the buzz. "If you cut me…," I threatened.

"Hey, girl. I do this to my face every day," he answered, the razor coming closer.

I shut my eyes and felt the metal glide in short strokes. "Easy, careful…"

And little by little, it was done. Perfectly.

I stood and Mike gathered me into his arms. "You're beautiful, Lin. Absolutely beautiful." Then he kissed me. A kiss right out of the best romance novel ever written. A kiss that made my heart race, head swim and lasted forever. His shiny armor beckoned right then.

"Wow. Perfect timing."

"I aim to please," he replied with a grin. "So, how about a main event?"

Now, I took the lead, and we went straight to our bedroom. I may have had cancer, but I wasn't dead yet and didn't intend to be.

#

Betty made her debut at work the next morning. I knew she was a close match, a real doppelgänger head of hair, but honestly, didn't anyone on staff notice she wasn't me? All I got was one or two "Your hair looks good," kind of comments, exactly the same as anyone would make about a new style or cut. Even my friend and boss, Kate, wouldn't have noticed had I not purposefully touched my head and struck a pose several times.

These non-reactions reinforced the fact that, like a volatile, hormone-challenged teenager, I thought the spotlight shone on me, that everyone's focus was on Linda. As an adult, I should have remembered that most people are into themselves. They're focused on their own lives, tasks and busy days. It would take a true oddity to divert their attention. Maybe if I'd walked in bald…

So much for staff. When you're a "real teacher" in a "real school,"—as my students described their program—all eyes focus on you. Just as Dr. B was the fulcrum around which everything turned in his office, I was the fulcrum in the classroom. My adult students, ranging in age from eighteen to over fifty, missed nothing.

"Ms. Linda, your hair's different. How come you're wearing a wig?"

In thirty seconds, Betty was outed in the classroom! I'd have been a fool not to take advantage of the opening my students gave me, so I simply told them the truth.

"But, I intend to be here every day, and I expect you to do the same. If I'm not feeling energetic sometimes, you'll understand why. But our work continues just like always. The GED exam doesn't care about cancer, so we can't either."

I meant every word. My homeless students came from fractured backgrounds and were trying to super-glue their lives together. They were dealing with shelter, food, clothing, health and family issues. Education came under the heading of life goals. The classroom provided a safe respite where they could move through the curriculum as quickly or slowly as they needed to.

I had been with this group for three months, and they were now seeing results of their efforts via a tangible tracking system where we checked off topics they'd mastered. They were marching toward their exams and diploma, believing in themselves perhaps for the first time in their recent history. I wouldn't risk a setback for them by *kvetching*.

I didn't have time for *cancer*. I had more important things to do. The thought blew me away, and in that moment, I realized I hadn't stopped living. My life was not on hold. My life continued with cancer relegated to a corner of it.

Denise stood. "If Ms. Linda is here every day, then we can be here, too. And maybe we can help her."

"It's a deal," I said, wondering what in the world she had in mind. Maybe wash our old-fashioned kind of blackboards? Denise had claimed the others' attention, speaking about classroom chores, and their true concern for me easily equaled or topped mine for them. There we were, mostly a group of adult women representing every race and ethnic group in America, all with hopes and dreams, all bleeding red under the skin and all potential targets of the disease that had zapped me. So, on a personal level, I realized that my war was their war, too.

I also realized that being in the classroom— teaching, advising, connecting with students—was an even better therapy for me than writing. Working in adult education had been my career for many years. Being engaged with students was normal for me. And I wanted "normal." I yearned for the ordinariness of my days. So I clung to the routines and embraced my habits and rituals of classroom life. There was also an added bonus in the workplace: interacting with others made time speed by. Poof! Lunchtime arrived. Poof! Four o'clock came, and I was in my car, heading home. Thanks to Betty—and Denise—I'd had a very good "reveal" day.

CHAPTER EIGHT

WHERE WOULD I BE WITHOUT MY FRIENDS?

My Aunt Ethel's motto about friendship: Don't be lazy. Pick up the phone and make the call. Her friendships reached back decades in the era before email and social networking, before Mark Zuckerburg had been a glint in his mother's eye. Facebook? What's that?

Mike and I had moved to Houston five years before cancer struck. Our friends in Worcester, Massachusetts, where we'd lived for twenty-three years and raised our boys, remained major figures in our lives and our reporting loop. Teddy, Margo, Sue, LinO—we'd connected with people in the community and at work, both with couples and, for me, some single girlfriends. After we made those initial calls to New England, I learned that my dynamic friend, Teddy Grossman, must have read Aunt Ethel's rules for life.

Every Saturday morning, without fail, the phone rang, and there was my little cheerleader "just checking up on you." Whether our chats lasted two minutes or twenty didn't matter. Whether I'd had a great week or a lousy one didn't matter. All that mattered—and warmed my heart when I went to bed each Friday night—was knowing I'd be speaking with Teddy the next morning. Our friendship needed no tests. We'd already formed a strong bond not only with each other, but between our husbands as well. Nightly walks through the neighborhood, Sunday dinners together and those approach-avoidance aerobics classes—*oy*. But we went every week, sweating and gasping for breath together, and ties strengthened. The content of those phone conversations was secondary to the love that flowed through the wires. Sometimes, friendships develop into sisterhoods born not of genes, but of choice.

#

In Houston, I was lucky enough to add to my coterie of chosen sisters. Phyllis and I met a month after I arrived in town. My entire family attended a new member open house at the temple we were joining. I walked up to a group of women deep in conversation about mahjong, a game I loved. Phyllis was going to teach a new group, and as we chatted, I volunteered to help her. A friendship ignited. Sometimes two people just hit it off immediately, and that's the way it was with us—and our husbands as well. How lucky can I get?

Phyllis makes things happen; she's a planner. Parties—large or intimate. Sunday outings. Family events. Shopping trips. Dinners—at home or in restaurants. Not once during my treatments did Phyllis ever exclude us from any social event she organized, whether a simple home-cooked dinner, a group dining out or a girls-only shopping jaunt. She never assumed I couldn't make it. Instead, she always asked first and allowed me to make the decision to go or not. Being thoughtful and inclusive is her style.

Despite her lovely invitations, she couldn't count on me to have a good opinion of any restaurant! After two or three chemo treatments, my taste buds were definitely unreliable. This became obvious after dining at an informal Middle Eastern place when the other five people with me praised the meal to the heavens. Delicious, delicious, delicious.

"Really?" I asked. "Then I must have gotten a ruined portion. It tasted funny." (Not that I ever ate an entire serving anyway.)

"Funny how?" asked Phyllis.

"Just off. Sort of like…like metal. Yeah, that's it. A metallic taste."

"It's the chemo," Mike said immediately. "You're in deep now."

"Thanks. Very comforting." I'd forgotten about that possibility, another damn chemo complication. "I am so sick of this. It's like there's no escape. And I love Middle Eastern food." Cancer, I had cancer! *Another reminder.*

Note to self: Get used to it.

Phyllis patted my arm. "It'll be over soon, and we'll come back when your taste buds are normal again. Don't worry. We like this place a lot—you'll be doing us a favor."

I had to laugh. She'd brought me back to normalcy. By her actions, support and generosity of spirit, she had done me untold favors and now offered another: the privilege of repaying the kindnesses. We both knew the "favor" was incidental, to make me feel better. So what? Phyllis became another sister-by-choice, just by being Phyllis.

#

I met Pat Rosen at my very first West Houston RWA chapter meeting in January 1996, six months after I'd arrived in town. By coincidence, it was her first meeting, too. Romance Writers of America is a national organization with chapters all over the United States and Canada. Houston is a large enough city to support three such groups. At that time, Pat and I were novice writers, trying to learn as much as possible to improve our craft. At each month's meeting, which included writing workshops, we tended to gravitate toward one another, and I thought of her as a friend in no time.

Smart, smart, smart. So smart and filled with common sense, I hired her to teach the GED class in a large adult education program I managed at that time where my responsibilities included hiring great staff. Pat's college degrees were supplemented by her eleven years as a high school French teacher in New Jersey. A perfect choice for both the students and me. They flourished, and I was able to relax knowing Pat was in the classroom.

Beyond work, Pat and I became writing buds, and for several years shared a hotel room at the summer RWA national conferences. In 2001, I trusted her with my secret, the only other writer in the group besides the four published authors who'd given me advice in the beginning. By then, I knew that telling Pat a secret was equivalent to throwing a coin down a deep well—it would go no further.

I trusted her, period. After all, sharing a room could have been awkward, but was not. Betty and her Styrofoam form were with me. I wore chemo caps at night, and sometimes pulled them off. Sure, they were lightweight, but they bothered my ears. In addition, I suffered from summer allergies despite using non-drowsy antihistamines. Would it be a one-tissue-box day or two?

Pat had her own problems. She was profoundly hard-of-hearing and wore two hearing aides. I'd already trained myself to face her when we spoke and tap her arm to get her attention. At the end of our exhausting conference days, she'd deposit her hearing aides in their case and fall asleep immediately. I've never witnessed anything like it. She could have earned an Olympic gold medal in the Falling Asleep Quickly category if there'd been one. From, "Good night, Linda," to dreamland in a nanosecond.

Between my bald head and her lousy ears, we were well-matched friends and roommates, each with a unique understanding of being less than perfect. And moving on.

A breast cancer diagnosis ripples through our friendship circles, shaking up everyone in our world. Some friends slowly disappear; I know they're frightened, and I hold no grudges. The loving friends, however, stay close despite their own fears. They are warriors, too. I couldn't have made it through without my friends.

CHAPTER NINE

BLANCHE PAYS A VISIT

Remember Blanche? My elderly, frail, uses-a-walker-or-a-cane mom. My strong, loving, supportive, can-figure-out-a-way mom. A mom who'd made up her mind to hop a plane from LaGuardia and fly to Houston. She wanted to see me "with her own eyes." I'm a mother, too, and understand exactly how she felt. However, I purposely scouted for dates when I'd be feeling my best—not the period following chemo when my malaise would be constant. Why should I put her through that? The best time was during the third week, just before the next treatment, but after my body had time to recoup. A tight window considering Blanche had her own medical appointments, but we managed it.

"When I pick you up in Houston, Mom, would you like me to wear my wig or a cap?" I asked on the phone a few days before her flight. By then, the city was horribly summer-hot, the wig was always hot—I pulled it off as soon as I got home from work each day—and I would have settled for a cap despite it annoying my ears.

But I wanted to give her the choice between seeing the iconic visual of a cancer patient or her easier memory of a "normal" me.

She paused for just a moment before choosing Betty. I wasn't surprised. In the midst of chaos, we grasp and cling to whatever bits of normal we can find. That's how I got through each day, and that's how she'd face seeing me.

So, with little fanfare, Blanche made wheelchair arrangements with the airports, and Judy got her onto the flight in NY. I found my way to the elevator in the baggage claim area of Houston's "big" airport—Bush International—where I'd meet her. The wait seemed interminable as I constantly compared my watch reading to the airport clock. Finally, the elevator door opened, and the porter wheeled my mother out.

She looked beautiful to me.

I looked beautiful to her.

Which proved the saying about beauty being in the eye of the beholder since neither one of us was cover girl material.

Hugging and kissing, joyous in reunion, we forgot about everything else for the moment. No cancer. No arthritis. No distance. But in the next moment, the enormity of her effort hit me like a ton. On her lap were a purse and a cane. I'd parked as closely as I could, but studying my mom gave me pause. She, however, had no qualms about the trek, and slowly, slowly we made our way to the parking lot.

She stayed with me for five days and wouldn't you know? Stuff happened. Surgical stuff. Even though I'd had the best of care, I was in pain. Real pain in my breast that I knew had nothing to do with cancer per se. Back I went to Dr. Joe, this time with Mom at my side. Ironic, wasn't it? Despite my best effort in choosing visiting dates so Mom could avoid up-close and personal witnessing, she got to see some action anyway. Murphy's law again.

After any surgery, a drain is put in place at the surgical site. The body doesn't like an empty space and injured tissue will fill it with a liquid known as *serous fluid.* The drain provides an outlet for the seroma (the pocket that is filled with fluid). Now, I had had a drain in place after the lumpectomy for a full twenty-four hours, which should have been long enough to avoid fluid building-up. It seems my body didn't get that memo.

"Do you want to stay here in the waiting room," I asked, "or come in with me?"

In she went, of course, craning her neck as I lay on the table while Dr. Joe inserted a needle to extract the fluid. Out it rushed, as eager to leave my body as I was to have it gone. The serous fluid filled two small basins, surprising everyone by the amount, but giving me immediate relief from pain. My spirits soared. In that moment, I felt normal—no pain, no nausea. Maybe we'd go out for dinner that night. Or maybe Mike would grill burgers or chicken, and I'd be able to eat a real meal. In that moment, anything was possible. It was the third week after chemo, a good time to be adventurous with my menu. I ate grilled chicken breast with cole slaw. A good choice. The sharp slaw permeated my metallic taste buds, and I almost finished the dinner.

Mom returned to NY reassured that her daughter would make out just fine. (Oops, there's that word again.) Before she left, she insisted on treating me to a house cleaning service for however long I wanted it. She'd employed cleaning help for many years herself, but in her case, such a service was both mandatory and well deserved as she climbed her professional career ladder. I'd never considered hiring household help. Mike and I were managing; the house wasn't a pigsty yet. But a week after Blanche's return to New York, a check arrived in my mailbox with a note that said, "For cleaning service. No arguments."

I didn't argue. As a mom, myself, I knew I'd want to ease my child's burdens in whatever way I could no matter his age. A mom is a mom forever. It's that simple. Blanche wanted the "privilege" of mothering me, of contributing to my well-being, of making sure I'd be as good as new. I wanted her to believe I'd be all those things. Knowing how stoically she handled her own crippling arthritis, I hoped she believed I'd do the same with my illness. In actuality, we were two different people. I'm a moaner and groaner. She suffers in silence. But from the time of her visit until the end of my treatments, we'd be conversing by phone. My voice could and would be strong. I vowed to make it so. And I did.

CHAPTER TEN

PASS THE SOUP, HOLD THE SANDWICH

Email to Author Friends:

May 10, 2001 - Two down, two to go. Halfway done and I'm doing fine.

I'd be fine as long as I had soup. After two chemo treatments, my menu of choice became more limited. Almost every day at lunchtime, however, Kate and our friend Craig, the IT specialist, ate lunch together at a variety of midtown Houston eateries. I hesitate to call them restaurants because customers are not served. We grab trays, order at the counter, and pick up our own food. My favorite place, Niko Niko's, started as a small Greek dive and then expanded to accommodate the hoards who showed up for lunch, beginning anytime after eleven. We tried to make it before noon. Parking was always hit-or-miss, despite the expanded lot, but that was Craig's problem. I was definitely a passenger.

Niko's offered a full Greek menu—sandwiches and dinner platters—chicken and beef souvlaki, gyros, wrapped grape leaves, pilaf, plus a million other items, and of course, the salad. Delicious salad with those salty black olives. More important to me, however, were the four soups offered every day. Four! All delicious. But my two favorites at the time were lentil (with a side of vinegar) and chicken (made with a little lemon) soup.

We usually sat at a shady outside table, enjoying the break from our windowless offices, enjoying the food and our own company. Naturally, conversation centered around the agency—Kate with her budgets, Craig with his computer issues, and me with my student worries. But we all had families, too, including kids meeting their special someones, so our chats encompassed our private lives as well. Never having lived in the south before, I took special enjoyment in lunching outside for much of the year. Mike, too, loved Texas life, in awe of the long growing season. We had a successful vegetable garden for the first time—as opposed to praying for one ripe tomato by Labor Day when we lived in Massachusetts.

If Kate, Craig and I didn't go to Niko's, we had to choose an alternative that offered soup. By the time my body metabolized the second round of chemo, I couldn't consider anything else. Although Craig may have been driving the van, I was driving the lunch bus. He and Kate went along with anything I wanted to eat, any place I wanted to go. In essence, they spoiled me. I knew it. They knew that I knew it. They teased; we laughed. They brought my spirits up focusing on anything but cancer. Lunchtimes were good times, especially with a cup of chicken soup and rice.

For dinner, Mike prepared more soup. Almost every night, he combined a package of Chinese egg drop soup with water and slowly poured a real egg into the pot. He whisked it around until it was hot, hot, hot. I liked soup piping hot. He poured half into a bowl and watched me eat one spoonful at a time. I could never finish the portions. I didn't know it at the time, but I was on my way to losing nine pounds through the three-month chemo process. Yeah, yeah, I know there's no such thing as being too rich or too thin, but I don't recommend this diet plan.

The constant queasiness reminded me of being pregnant with my oldest son. I didn't vomit then either, just felt seasick every single day. Maybe it's a lousy comparison to talk about brand new life while fighting a battle against death. As thrilled as I was about being pregnant, about becoming a mother, I simply couldn't eat much while Andy was growing inside me. My sweet boy—a man now—is a light in my life. But my memory is supported with facts. Although I didn't lose weight while pregnant, I did gain only fourteen pounds. So, overcoming queasiness is not my strength. During chemo, I relied on the classroom and my writing projects to distract me and I was grateful to have these important distractions. With my mind engaged, I didn't think about myself.

My students knew the score, however, and definitely had me on their minds. With two treatments behind me, I returned to the classroom after lunch one day, and as usual, dropped my purse in my desk drawer and got ready to start the afternoon's agenda. Without warning, however, Denise—the student who wanted to help me when I first told the class about my illness—closed the door, shut off the lights, and announced her intentions.

"We will now hold a prayer meeting for Ms. Linda. You all know she's got the breast cancer, so we're going to pray." The intrepid Denise didn't give her classmates a choice, and no one left the room. She turned to me and told me to sit down and not do anything. To say she surprised me into silence—a pretty hard achievement—would be the truth. My lips were zipped.

Without hesitation, this forty-six year old African-American woman—homeless, poor, in recovery and struggling to pass the math section of her GED exam—started beseeching the Lord on my behalf. Preaching, beseeching and invoking. She preached to her classroom congregation. She beseeched God. She invoked Jesus. She prayed aloud and she prayed loudly. She paced, she pointed, her arms rising and falling with her trope. The classroom became her church. Words flowed from her heart and mouth like water down a stream (Why couldn't she make her words flow in an essay?), and as though choreographed, the other students were on their feet in no time, invoking their own "Amens."

Now, as you may have deduced, I'm an ordinary Jewish woman originally from New York who happened to be living in Houston, Texas. To say I felt overwhelmed by this outpouring is an understatement. A fish out of water—that's what I was. What did I know about being the object of a heartfelt African-American prayer service? Nothing. Absolutely nothing. But it didn't matter. I felt the warmth and love in that room on that day, and I've never forgotten it. I never will forget it.

When she finished the service, which ran for almost twenty minutes, Denise turned the room lights back on, walked to her seat, and said, "Okay, Ms. Linda. We're looking out for you, sort of how you look out for us. I'm finished now, and you can teach again."

I needed a moment to find my voice. "You were amazing. All of you were amazing. Thank you. Thank you very, very much because every prayer helps."

When the heart pumps love, does anything else

matter?

At our graduation ceremony, all my students received not only a copy of Harper Lee's iconic American work, *To Kill a Mockingbird*, but also autographed copies of my own novels. They were so proud of those signed books, so proud of their teacher. I hope they were prouder of themselves.

CHAPTER ELEVEN

LOOK MA, NO HAIR...ANYWHERE

Email to Author Friends:

May 31, 2001 – Three down, one to go. I'm hanging on.

The Red Devil wore boxing gloves after my third chemo infusion. The malaise was unremitting; I dreaded the third day knockout when my body had metabolized the drugs, and I lay on my stomach, groaning. Although I celebrated being at the halfway point on the calendar, I still had another six weeks of coping with the nausea. Until this point, except for being as bald as a GE light bulb, nausea was the main side effect I dealt with on a daily basis.

After the third infusion, however, I lost my eyebrows and lashes. Even my glasses couldn't protect my eyes from airborne irritants. Specs of dust were a menace. My lids became red and inflamed. I started wearing sunglasses most of the time, hoping for better outdoor protection. Salve helped.

At about the same time, most of my nasal hair disappeared too. Have I mentioned I have a ton of allergies and usually keep a tissue box nearby? Without nasal hair, there is no warning before your nose actually runs. The watery mucus just drips out—on the floor, desk, or lap—wherever you happen to be. So it was with me. I learned to carry a tissue in my hand, or belt or pocket—always. I'd already placed a box of tissues in my classroom for the students and me, but now I put a box in Kate's office as well and kept a couple of spare boxes in the car…just in case.

Here's the upside to all this hair stuff: no more shaving legs! And as for the bikini area? Forget about shaving that too.

And while we're on that subject…

Whether it was to defy death, or whether it came from the love Mike and I had shared for so many years, I'm not sure. But our sex life was fabulous. I mean powerful. No holds barred. As though we were still in our twenties. As though we were tasting the sweetness of first love, discovering its wonder and joy as we'd done years ago. Maybe we were trying to recapture all those firsts in order to prove we were still here. Whatever the underlying truth, we discovered that life waited for us. For him and for me.

It's ironic that literature refers to the moments after climax as "the little death." I get it. I really do get it. But to me, making love was a reaffirmation of life, and I didn't need the threat of death to make me appreciate living. I didn't need to "stop and smell the roses." I've always made time for that. The big things in my life have not gone unnoticed; neither have the little things. But sometimes, I'm in a hurry. Sometimes, I'm distracted. Sometimes, I'm too tired. When my knight and I made love during those months, we took all the time we wanted. Or needed. And it was good.

Mike said that I usually had a shit-eatin' grin on my face as we cuddled afterwards. Nude of hair, I thought I looked like a ten-year-old. He thought I looked like a porn star. Men!

CHAPTER TWELVE

THE NEVER-ENDING HOME STRETCH

I received my third chemo on May 31st, slogged through my usual lousy Sunday, then a lousy Monday, and an entire lousy week. The second week wasn't much better, a disappointment. Usually, by the end of the second week, I'd start bouncing back. But this time, I was dragging—with no energy or appetite. The bed looked awfully inviting, but I had to go to work, not only in the classroom but also at the computer.

I delivered my second manuscript on time and got approval for my third book, *The Apple Orchard*, scheduled for publication in July 2002, which meant my drop-dead due date was in November, five months away. I'd suggested the date because the story was already partly written at the time I signed the contract. My concentration was wonky, however, scattered by the effects of my treatments. I worried about on-time delivery. I worried about quality. I worried about failing—a totally unacceptable concept.

My target date for Chemo #4 was June 21st. No matter how awful I felt, I wanted nothing to interfere with getting my last treatment. *My last one*. Last. Last. Last. It would be over, and I'd start to rebound. At that point, I wasn't concerned about the thirty days of radiation to follow. Saying good-bye the Red Devil, a tough ally, was my only goal. The accumulation of chemicals had taken me to the point of crying "uncle." Enough already.

When I was a kid, I went to school every day unless I had a bona fide fever. A simple cold wouldn't qualify as a day off, even with a running nose. As an adult, I followed the same pattern. If I wasn't actually vomiting, I couldn't stay home. Before now, I managed to overcome the queasiness and continue with my work. Work had become therapeutic, a calming force, providing my normal environment. But this particular three-week interval left normal in the dust. I felt awful. Horrible. I felt like shit.

I visited Dr. B's office every Thursday for blood count monitoring and Procrit shots to boost the red blood count if needed. Every week, the nurses and I would catch up with each other. I bonded with all three RNs, each one a credit to her profession. I did receive my Procrit during this interval and hoped it would help me bounce back. No such luck.

Two weeks after the third treatment, I showed up at Dr. B's office for my blood count check. Grace met me at the waiting room door and welcomed me with a smile.

"How are you today?"

That's all it took. One innocent question and I burst into tears. "Not good, not good."

"Uh-oh. Come on back here with me. Let's see what going on."

I followed her to an exam room, and in a few

minutes, we had our answers. "Going on" was a temp of 102 degrees and low blood counts plus a lot of tears, both physical and mental fatigue and more weight loss. In short, I was a mess.

Dr. B came in and examined me. My lymph nodes weren't swollen, no sore throat, but he didn't like the fever—an infection was brewing. I received my Procrit shot, a prescription for antibiotics and instructions.

"Call us tomorrow," Dr. B said. "We need to monitor you. Fevers are critical indicators and with low blood counts, some patients are better off in the hospital for a few days."

All I heard was the word "hospital." No way, no way, no way! Hospitals were for very sick people, not for me.

"But my last chemo is set for next Thursday," I wailed, my one-track mind still on the main goal. "I don't want to postpone it. I want it over with."

"My aim is to get you through this as a healthy woman," he said. "No matter what date is on the calendar."

Grace patted my shoulder. "If your temp drops with the antibiotics, you'll keep the appointment, and we'll see where the counts are then."

I left the office, called Kate and went straight home. Even I knew when enough was enough. With a bona fide fever, missing work was allowed.

The fever broke over the weekend. I finished the antibiotics, went back to work, and with hope blooming, showed up for my last infusion. Blood draws were done first, of course, and as I waited for the results, my anxiety increased. Sometimes, I thought the chemo teamed up with the cancer to try to kill me. Adria and Cytoxan don't differentiate between cancer cells and healthy cells—they target all fast-growing cells. In our bodies, hair follicles and the cells lining the stomach reproduce rapidly and are therefore killed off by these drugs, leaving patients bald and nauseous. And sick. Like I'd been sick. I suppose I was a textbook case—not such a bad thing to be. But sitting in Dr. B's office, waiting for the blood draw results, I had a hard time seeing the big picture. I wanted the last damn treatment; I wanted to put this all behind me.

Grace came in, holding the printout of my count readings, and shaking her head. "Not today. We don't want you back where you were last week."

And suddenly, what the hell were another few days? I felt okay—maybe not strong enough to move mountains, but well enough for a nice weekend with Mike minus the usual miserable Sunday.

My rescheduled final appointment was for the following Tuesday, five days out. Despite my new-found sanguinity, I hoped five days were enough for my body to build up a healthy blood supply. I sure didn't want a second postponement, especially with Romance Writers of America's national conference in New Orleans the next month. My friend, Pat Rosen, and I had planned to make the six-hour road trip and room together at the hotel. I knew I'd need my strength.

CHAPTER THIRTEEN

BIG PLANS IN THE BIG EASY

Email to Author Friends:

Tuesday, June 26, 2001- Hey y'all!
Four down; Zero to go. It's over, over, over!
See you at the conference next month.

During the summer of each year, Romance Writers of America holds a conference to which all members—published authors or not—are invited. A few major publishers usually sponsor part of the conference, such as providing lovely tote bags for everyone, but writers pay a pretty hefty conference fee in addition to the costs of hotel and transportation. Incredibly, price seemed to be no factor to aspiring, newly-published or established authors. About two thousand members attend, and because we focus on the romance genre, the attendees are mostly women. Two thousand women have clout.

Most of the Men's restrooms now boast "Ladies" signs, and inside, the urinals are covered—to protect our delicate sensibilities?

Several years before I got the "call" about Amanda Shaw, and the call from Dr. Joe, I had gone to the RWA conference in Dallas. Four women shared a room for four nights; we drove up together from Houston not only with our luggage, but with bags of food—healthy and not so much—to try to save money. Cost was a factor for all of us, and no one was ashamed to admit it. Everyone was in high spirits, so we all got along beautifully.

That conference was an eye-opener for me, a wonderful, enriching experience in all things writing related. My focus was on learning craft. From eight o'clock in the morning until five o'clock in the afternoon, I attended workshops. Never missed an hour. I'd shelled out hard-earned money for this opportunity to learn and wanted to take advantage of every offering RWA provided. For me, attending the conference was an investment in my second career.

I had a lot to learn. The craft of fiction is about how to weave the elements of a story together—plot, character, motivation, dialogue, conflict, setting, backstory—the list goes on. The pleasure of reading a worthy novel—a can't-put-it-down-book—might make you wonder just how difficult this writing business can be. Let's just say, it all looks easy before you put your own fingers to the keyboard and try to do it. At that point, you'll discover how difficult writing a "simple" story really is. The age-old conflict of Theory vs. Reality rears its head once more. To quote F. Scott Fitzgerald, "All good writing is swimming under water holding your breath."

I wanted my writing to improve, so three weeks after my last chemo, Pat Rosen and I (and Betty) eagerly arrived at the New Orleans hotel. Despite the late hour, the heat and humidity were so high—higher than Houston's—I was "swimming under water" without having written a word! After stepping out of the car, I could barely breathe and instantly decided never to leave the hotel's air-conditioned premises.

Within twenty-four hours, I realized that despite the air-conditioning, I was not only sweltering in my wig but still couldn't breathe. My allergies had morphed into monsters, and although I downed anti-histamines, I used up a box of tissues that first day. Again, I was a mess. I could have used a little emotional support, even if it was just a simple, "How're you doing, Linda?" But none of my writing friends knew the truth. Instead, I received a lot of compliments on how great I looked. Between my trusty brown eyebrow pencil and Betty's blonde magnificence, I probably did look pretty good. I loved the irony, but hated feeling so crappy. At my weakest moment, I considered calling Mike to pick me up or taking a bus back home. Maybe I would have, except I had a professional conflict.

Several weeks prior to the conference, I had made an appointment to pitch a four-book series not only to my own editor, but also to the senior editor of the *Harlequin Superromance* line. I liked writing Supers because of their longer page count, which allowed room for subplots and deeper character exploration. I loved my miniseries idea and did not want to cancel that appointment! So, my stubbornness kicked in, and I stayed at the hotel. I'm a writer, and writers write, preferably with a contract. I couldn't lose this opportunity to meet privately with my editors during the conference, especially after all the work done beforehand.

I'd invented a place called Pilgrim Cove. I'd invented four couples whose heroes and heroines would find their way to each other through the nexus of Sea

View House. I'd invented an entire population of townspeople, including the ROMEOS—the Retired Old Men Eating Out—who breakfasted each morning at the Diner on the Dunes. I'd also created two huge hand-made colorful visuals so the editors could see the concepts at a glance. The Saturday appointment meant I had to hang tough from Wednesday night on. Hanging tough meant keeping a smile on my face and Betty on my head.

That hot blonde earned me unending compliments. I was amazed no one ever guessed my secret, not even other Houston authors whom I'd befriended through the years. In general, writers are pretty observant folks who examine details. But Betty reflected my natural color and style, and friends thought I was having some great hair days. *Oy.*

In the beginning, going to bed was the best part of the conference. Thank God for Pat. Between her hearing aides and my wig, we laughed away the fatigue and tension. Where extroverts thrive in crowds, introverts get exhausted. I believe Pat and I possessed a bit of both descriptors in our personalities, but handling a constant two thousand people, day and night, is a lot to ask.

By Friday morning, my allergies had calmed down, my energy level had improved, and I reconsidered attending my publisher's big party that evening, an annual event at the conference. This year, it was being held in the French Quarter at a charming and famous restaurant eight long blocks away from the hotel. If I shared a taxi, I figured I could handle the party itself. My mistake.

Although I did share a ride with a group of other authors, I needed to leave an hour after arriving. The open ironwork balconies and French doors lost their charm when the heavy night air outdoors overpowered the air-conditioning system indoors. I believe the restaurant had two or three levels with a warren of rooms, each one more crowded than the last. Music blared all evening. At times, I sought more quietude on the balconies where I could actually have a conversation.

In the end, however, I admitted defeat and made my way to the exit. I was surprised to be part of a finely feathered flock, also anxious to fly back to the Marriott. I wished we could have spread real wings and flown. No taxis now. Most of us walked barefoot down the dark narrow streets, some front stoops strewn with trash and dozing residents. Our shoes lost the battle to swollen tootsies in the humidity of the ninety-five degree evening.

None of my subsequent visits to New Orleans are illuminated in my memory as much as this one. Certainly my chemo race against the calendar, dependence on the perfect but hot Betty, and surviving the stifling weather played big parts. However, I'm quite sure that visit to the Big Easy stands out because I did get that four-book contract and started to believe the unbelievable: I was a legitimate writer, I could put a story together, I had a future.

Pat enjoyed a good conference, too, and we prolonged our lovely time by lingering over a meal on the way home. The success at the conference kept my spirits up as I got ready for thirty days of radiation.

CHAPTER FOURTEEN

X MARKS THE SPOT

Houston, Texas
August 2001

I'd been told that radiation would be part of my arsenal of weapons against cancer, but I'd pushed it to the back of my mind throughout my surgery and chemo infusions. At the time of the lumpectomy, radiation therapy was far away—many months away—a timeframe I couldn't contemplate. During chemo, my goal remained steadfast: get through each day whole, mentally and physically. Each day's survival counted as a small victory.

Several days after arriving home from New Orleans, however, radiation treatment became my newest reality. "Far away" had morphed into "right now," and I found myself lying on a table, being mapped with a purple Magic Marker.

"The X-ray showed us the exact location of your heart and lungs so we can avoid those areas," said Dr. S as he marked me with semi-permanent, tattooed dots.

"I like that idea a lot," I said.

"I'm showing the technicians exactly where to aim the beam safely."

To me, radiation was an insurance policy. Dr. Joe might have cut out all the cancer cells; the chemo might have killed off stragglers, but no one could guarantee any of it. Radiation was another weapon against the cancer returning.

"You'll be coming here Monday through Friday for six weeks," he continued. "But the radiation only lasts a minute or so."

Stopping off at the facility every day for a minute or two sounded like a royal pain, which is why I'd chosen a doctor near home rather than near my job.

"Someone in my son's office had radiation," I proffered casually, "and was hardly able to work for three weeks because of exhaustion."

"Well, some patients do get very tired. Unfortunately, we can't predict who will and who won't."

"Her skin burned, too," I added, "and my skin is very fair. I'm a red lobster after five minutes in the sun."

"It happens, but not to everyone. Keep some aloe on hand if you like." Just like with all other treatments, I was again playing a wait-and-see game with side effects. Bad enough to be one-and-seven-eighths, I just hoped my breast wouldn't shrivel up entirely!

There was one more risk—a small one—I haven't mentioned yet, a risk with both chemo and radiation: the chance of developing leukemia later on in life. Chemo is known to be a higher risk factor than radiation therapy, but I had no choice. These two therapies would increase my chance of survival. Period.

No one offered the gift of survival with a money-back guarantee, however, not even Dr. B, who I totally trusted. Despite doing "all the right things," I might be unlucky in the end. On the other hand, I might have opted for just the lumpectomy, avoiding the chemo and radiation, and wound up in the same unlucky place. A patient's fight to eliminate her breast cancer boils down to considering medical advice and statistics, making choices and hoping for the best.

I think it's all a crapshoot, and we play the odds with more than money. But unlike Las Vegas, these odds are in our favor rather than the dealer's, as long as we hang tough with our therapies. As for my burning boob concern? My skin remained as white as always during the radiation treatments. Skeptical, I asked the technicians to confirm the machine was working properly, and it was.

When I looked at my body in the mirror after the radiation therapy ended, I was amazed to see my normal self. If it weren't for the obvious dimple left by the lumpectomy, no one could have guessed what my body had been through. My breast had dodged a bullet. Or so I thought.

CHAPTER FIFTEEN

A WEDDING AND A FUNERAL

In March of 2002, exactly nine months after my last chemo, Mike and I celebrated the marriage of Andy and Pauline. Our eldest son had met his bride-to-be at a professional conference in Florida where Pauline happened to live. Their wedding took place along the beautiful gulf coast of that state.

To say I was a bit *verklempt* would be an understatement. I'd lived to see this day! The bride was beautiful, the groom handsome and my new four-year-old grandson adorable. I felt beautiful too, if a bit self-conscious. My dependable "Betty" was back in Houston, and I sported a natural three-inch style—darker than I was used to and sprinkled with silver strands. I didn't care. I was on my way to normalcy.

Almost the entire family gathered for this event. From Mike's side and mine came cousins, aunts and uncles all wanting to celebrate happiness. Lifetime friends came, too, and the east coast was well represented by Teddy, Richie, Margo, Mel, the two other

Mikes, Jackie and Marcy.

Most precious perhaps was watching the grandmas, Blanche and Dee, escorted by my younger sons, march down the aisle to witness their eldest grandchild's marriage. Standing tall, walking with slow, deliberate steps and wearing a big smile, my mom conquered and enjoyed her world despite it being in shadow without my dad. He passed away in 1989, thirteen years earlier. A natural extrovert, Dad turned strangers into friends and every family event into a party. He certainly would have partied the night away in Florida. When he died, Mom gave me the gold wedding ring he'd worn throughout their marriage.

"Save it for the boys," she'd said, "to use for their wedding ceremonies, whenever they will be." David and Ricky were still in their teens at the time; Andy had just turned twenty.

Before leaving Houston for the wedding, I'd taken Dad's gold band from my special jewelry case. A unique poignancy enveloped us as we listened to Andy and Pauline exchange vows and watched Papa Manny's ring slip onto his grandson's finger, a symbol of a long, loving marriage and family continuity. I so wished Dad had lived to see this day, but contented myself knowing he was with us in spirit, in our hearts.

As for Grandma Dee—my mother-in-law enjoyed the wedding as much as she could. Mike's dad had been suffering with Alzheimer's and complications from diabetes for several years and remained in New York. At ten o'clock that evening, after the ceremony and toward the end of the wedding festivities, we received the news that Papa John had passed away.

Besides a lifetime of family memories, he left behind stories to tell and letters to Dee from his various outposts in Europe during World War II. My mother-in-law gave these letters to me to see "if you can do something with them." I'd doubted it at the time, but later changed my mind as I browsed through their correspondence. Most of Dee's letters contained ordinary family news, but my eye paused on John's descriptions, especially a beautiful paragraph describing a Belgium barn where his unit rested for twenty-four hours. That one paragraph inspired me to write the book that remains closest to my heart, *The Soldier and the Rose*, published in 2007.

After Pauline and Andy's wedding ceremony, I slipped my dad's ring back into my purse, keeping it safe for the future. Andy had two younger brothers, and they'd need Papa Manny's blessing as well. I looked forward to those big occasions, imaginary though they were. They'd be a hell of a lot more fun than chemo treatments.

Mike and I just starting out, happy but clueless

Pat Rosen and me at our very first RWA conference in Dallas in 1999. I was going through a hair flat-iron phase.

At a signing in February 2001 for my very first book, Love, Money and Amanda Shaw, a Harlequin Superromance. I had already been diagnosed, but hadn't started treatment yet, so that's my real hair.

Me and Mike with our close friends Teddy and Richie Grossman at a signing in 2001 at Walden Books.

Me – and Betty – six months after my first surgery, three months after chemo, giving a workshop at the West Houston RWA Chapter in 2001.

Mike and me in Florida at our oldest son's wedding in March of 2002. This was nine months after the last chemo of my first cancer bout, so the growth is really eight month's worth.

Grandma Blanche (Left) and Grandma Dee with the bride and groom in 2005. This was the year my cousin advised me to get tested, but life was good and I didn't want to think about it.

CHAPTER SIXTEEN

IS IGNORANCE TRULY BLISS?

Houston, Texas
2002-2005

Writing. Teaching. Saturday nights with friends. That pattern became a constant in my life along with my quarterly, then semi-annual appointments with Dr. B.

I was finishing up a manuscript for publication in 2003 and still had to write the four books for the Pilgrim Cove series, which would be released in 2004 and 2005. My GED classes were flourishing, and I was feeling stronger, physically and mentally, every day. On the weekends, I was a writing warrior; during the week, I spouted and taught—believe it or not—basic chemistry and physics along with the more familiar English, math and social studies content of the exam.

Mike and I regained our balance as a couple that socialized with friends. I tried to put the cancer experience behind me. Every time a nightmare threatened, I made myself think about other things. Keeping busy became my passion.

"You're not Cleopatra this time," Mike said, referring to the often heard Queen of De-nial joke. "I think what you're doing is healthy. If you jump at every imagined shadow, you'll be scared all the time, and that's no way to live."So I kept my head down, kept my appointments with Dr. B and had a mammogram every December, my birthday month. I was calm the first two years because I knew the statistics. Breast cancer recurrences usually happened between the second and third year out. When I was clean in 2004, I began to relax.

At about the same time, unfortunately, I discovered that breast cancer was making an appearance among some of my cousins. Susie and I were first cousins; our fathers had been brothers. She had survived a bout of breast cancer eleven or twelve years before mine showed up. The other affected cousins were two or three degrees removed and all on my dad's side of the family. All lived in the New York area except for one in California, and I saw them infrequently—less than once a year—especially since Mike and I had moved to Texas.

Some diseases seem to run in different families. Diabetes, hypertension, heart disease and cancer are common ones. I'd noticed that members of Dad's family seemed to be hit with cancer more frequently than a typical American family, but neither my dad nor his two siblings ever had the disease, and I hadn't grown up worrying about it.

Now, however, I started to notice particulars. Susie had a recurrence after I was finished with my treatments in 2001. My dad's first cousin, Sheila, was hit at about the same time. And then her daughter followed suit. Evy was only about thirty-years-old at the time, happily married and with a young son.

When I saw Sheila a couple of years later, she was walking with a cane. Her cancer had spread, and the chemo/radiation treatments had been difficult. Most of her pain, however, was for her daughter. She said to me, "You must take a blood test. Ask your doctor. Evy and I are carriers of a gene mutation that can cause breast cancer, and the gene runs in families. You've got to find out if you have it."

And here's where Cleopatra made her appearance. I didn't want to know. I'd put my cancer experience behind me and didn't want to think about it anymore. I rationalized that I didn't have any daughters. Every medical questionnaire I'd ever filled out until now asked about my mother, sisters, maternal aunts and grandmothers. Not one asked about my dad's side of the family in relation to breast cancer. I thought my sweet Sheila was over-reacting to her own situation—not that I blamed her—and I mentally separated myself from her diagnosis. I told myself her experience was a fluke. Sheila's mother—my dad's aunt Esther—had never had cancer. So how could she have passed it on to Sheila?

The increase in all types of cancers was blamed on environmental causes—contaminated water supplies, acid rain, industrial air pollutants. I'd tried to connect those dots myself, but in the end, accepted that I was probably the "one-in-eight-women" statistic quoted for breast cancer in those years. A random hit. I'd played Russion Roulette and lost.

#

Keep on Trucking

I'd begun writing *The House on the Beach*, the first book in the Pilgrim Cove series. The heroine, Laura McCloud, echoed my breast cancer experience. Before the story opens, Laura's fiancé has broken their engagement. She doesn't blame him. The hero, Matt Parker, a widower with two young boys, had lost his first wife to breast cancer. But he'd already fallen in love with Laura, and though he tries to walk away, finds himself returning to her. In the romance genre, the protagonists are guaranteed a "happily ever after." Matt would be happier with Laura than without her, and shows up at the oncologist's office when she has another scare, to learn as much as he can.

Although it seemed like a great idea at the time, writing this book almost killed me. With every medical scene, I relived my own memories, crying as I typed, winding up totally exhausted. While it's true that a little part of the author is reflected in every book she writes, giving this much of my soul went beyond reasonable, beyond my own expectation. But it was too late to renege; I'd gone to great lengths to get this contract and had already signed it. No one had forced me; the story had been my idea!

In a place way down deep inside me, that special place where truth resides, a tiny voice urged me to *buck up and write now, cry later.* I listened because the voice made sense. Finally, procrastination was an asset. My tears would have to wait.

In romance novels, the main characters must have challenges that keep them apart until they're overcome. *Boy meets girl, boy loses girl, boy gets girl* is the overall structure of any romance. Before tackling this story, I had read only two other series romances that offered innate medical issues for the hero and heroine to overcome. One was Fay Robinson's amazing book, *A Man Like Mac*, where the hero is a paraplegic in a wheelchair. And the other was Judith Arnold's wonderful, warm and funny tribute to her own sister titled *Barefoot In the Grass*, where the heroine has breast cancer. If there were other stories of this type in category romance at that time, I was unaware of them. As far as I knew, I was almost breaking new ground in my tiny corner of the literary world. (For the record, I'm discounting amnesia conditions of hero/heroine, found in many books, which is a storytelling device and not a natural medical condition for the character.)

Mike thought this book would be the best I'd produced to date.

"You've been in the trenches, Linda. You'll get it right. You're like an expert on the subject now, and the readers will trust you."

"Did I ask to be an expert?" I retorted. "I'd be happy to give up that title, thank you very much."

Despite Mike's encouragement, I wanted to kick myself for jumping into this project. I didn't need the agony, the tears. Why had I invented the damn story in the first place? Although I'd given some talks about my experience and had spoken to people on an individual basis, I'd purposely not volunteered at the hospital or with support groups. I didn't want to keep reliving my own "adventure." Now here I was, reliving it anyway.

I kept going. Kept writing. And in March 2004, Laura McCloud and Matt Parker, along with their Pilgrim Cove neighbors, made their debuts. Within a week, letters from readers began to arrive—both hand-written and emailed:

"Thank you for a heart warming and courageous story about battling breast cancer, its fears, stigma and yet allow the character to still dream of the future. I'm sending your book to my mother for she too is a breast cancer survivor…"

Sent by email

"Just a note to let you know I really enjoyed and

was greatly moved by the story "The House on the Beach." I know how it goes with illness, my husband had over 30 surgeries in our married life…"
Seattle, WA

"Linda: I am now 7 years, 10 months from diagnosis. Let's celebrate our breast cancer survivorship…"
Cleveland Heights, OH

"Thank you for writing this story. Only someone who's experienced the peaks and valleys of dealing with breast cancer can get the emotions down in black and white. As a 9-year breast cancer survivor, I felt especially close to Laura McCloud as she found her way through the aftermath of treatment while trying to maintain "normal" relationships with the people around her. A breast cancer survivor will always see the world in a different way, I think, but hopefully it will be a brighter world where every moment is savored."
Sent by email

"I admired the strength in Laura, and she made me think about life and how it can change a person in minutes. It reminded me of what I personally have to do to stay healthy. Thank you for that!"
From Canada

And finally this one, where real life and fiction met:

"I started the book last night. This is the first time I've picked up a book in a month…my husband has cancer and many doctor appointments. I did not read the back cover blurb first. My grandmother died of breast cancer in late February, and the last six months were very hard for her. We shared the same birthday and I loved her very much. When I started reading the book last night, I cried for the first time for my grandmother. Her name was Laura McCloud. Thank you."

Sent by email

Letters about this story kept arriving for several years as readers discovered the book. With each note, a corner of my heart tore a little as I finally understood the answer to my own question: I wrote *The House on the Beach* to connect with readers and offer hope.

Evidently, the story resonated with a lot of people. It won several prestigious romance industry awards including the Holt Medallion, The Award of Excellence, *Best Superromance* of 2004 as well as the Cataromance Reviewer's Choice Award.

So, was the stress worth it?

Yes—and with a bonus. I'd finally shrugged the "secret" from my shoulders and revealed the truth to my editors. And guess what? They wanted more book proposals from me! Either I was a total jerk or breast cancer had become part of the lexicon for women everywhere and couldn't be ignored or dismissed by anyone.

Initially, I believed the latter. The month of October had been set aside as Breast Cancer Awareness Month. Susan G. Komen For The Cure was thriving, and Race for the Cure was becoming a worldwide event. The American Cancer Society, the Breast Cancer Foundation website and many other research and fund-raising groups had bloomed in the public eye. In the late 1990s, breast cancer memoirs started hitting the market. And in 2001, six months after I was diagnosed, widely-read novelist and breast cancer survivor, Barbara Delinsky, published her non-fiction book, *UPLIFT: Secrets from the Sisterhood of Breast Cancer Survivors.* The book is filled with anecdotes and useful hints—"things a doctor doesn't say"—for those with the disease. All profits went, and still go, to her foundation at Mass General Hospital in Boston.

I hadn't been alone on my journey. My wonderful family and special friends were with me all the way. However, I'd been too distracted with my own battles to appreciate the stories appearing in the media by people I didn't know. Even when my dear friend Pat and the staff at my former job gave me a terrific memoir called *Bald in the Land of Big Hair* by Joni Rodgers, a gal living in Texas like I was, I didn't reach out to her. It would have been so easy to call or write, especially because we had a mutual friend. But no. That wasn't me. I waged a solitary war. It had been my choice, my comfort zone.

Maybe I'd been a total jerk after all.

CHAPTER SEVENTEEN

ROMANCE IN BLOOM

My youngest son had met his special lady on a Friday night at a bar in Manhattan while I was recuperating from my cancer treatments in Texas. Does the line, "across a crowded room," sound familiar? If you thought he swooped in to conquer, you would be right. Perhaps he muttered to himself Caesar's famous words, *veni, vidi, vici.* If so, I'm sure my delightful and intelligent daughter-in-law allowed herself to be caught and conquered.

A year later, Rick and Sandy were living with Grandma Blanche. That's right. You heard me. My mom was ahead of her time. But the kids had a cheap place to stay, and Grandma had the best company in the world, including nightly games of Rummycube.

Once again, life became a time of celebration as the seasons cycled around us. So far, each year had brought a clean mammogram, Mike and I were both working, finances were stable—which had not always been the case—and all three of our sons were gainfully employed, albeit in far flung states.

Happiness reached new heights with the birth of our first granddaughter in 2002. Aaron now had a baby sister. Mike and I rushed to Florida to meet this remarkable child—of course, she was remarkable—she was ours! And from that time on, visits to Florida became a regular event. Contemporary life has made distance a challenge for many families with parents and grown children picking up and following employment opportunities. Mike and I vowed not to allow the miles to hinder our relationship with our grandchildren. We became very familiar with Interstate 10 as we drove the straight thousand miles between Tampa and Houston. I should be more specific. Mike did the driving while I did everything else. He said driving was less boring than being a passenger. With our iPod playing music through the speakers, and my crochet projects, books, Sudoku and a laptop for writing to keep me busy, the trip became a piece of cake.

And speaking of cake...ta-da! Another wedding. Rick and Sandy tied the knot in July 2005. A beautiful affair with music, good food, friends and family. Grandma Blanche and Grandma Dee, looking like petite but elegant matriarchs, simply glowed as they watched the young couple together. My mom struggled, her walker at arm's length. But her smile never wavered, not even when Sandy placed Papa Manny's ring on Rick's finger. My dad would have been thrilled. He would have *kvelled,* the buttons bursting from his vest. Another full circle. Another reason to be *verklempt.*

I wore a strapless gown. Take that, lumpectomy!

#

Why Spoil a Good Run?

My December mammogram in 2005 was as clean as the proverbial whistle. As clean as new-fallen snow. Use any simile that works for a beautiful result. I was happy, very happy, except—my dear cousin, Susie, had died of leukemia in 2004, and I couldn't forget about my cousin Sheila and the advice she'd given me to get tested for the breast cancer gene mutation.

I'd brought the question to Dr. B that year, and he responded with a question of his own.

"What would you do about it if the result was positive?"

"Nothing." The reply flew from my mouth. Four years had passed, and I was healthy, more relaxed and looked almost like myself from the "before" days. Mike and I were making good use of my "magic buttons" in bed, and our intimate moments were as satisfying as ever. I couldn't imagine voluntarily giving up such hard-won normalcy and discounted the option.

"I can arrange for the test," Dr. B said, "but what's the point of knowing the outcome if you're not going to take action?"

I agreed with him. Furthermore, although the BRCA mutations had been identified about ten years earlier, researchers still didn't know everything. Why did some people with the mutation get breast cancer while others got ovarian? More significantly, why do some people with the mutation never get either? That's right. Not everyone with the mutation gets breast or ovarian cancer. I might have the gene mutation, or I might not. Furthermore, Susie had not been tested, nor had it ever come up in discussion with her. She'd been treated at Sloan-Kettering, a pre-eminent medical facility, and she'd shared everything with us. I found it easy to ignore the possibility, especially after celebrating

Rick and Sandy's marriage, the birth of a granddaughter and being so thankful that the children were thriving. They provided me with much happier topics on which to focus.

#

Changes and More Changes

After the publication of the four-book Pilgrim Cove series, my writing life continued at a slower pace—a good thing in many ways. Working a full-time day job and producing two books a year by writing nights and weekends got old after awhile. I needed some down time. Some fun time. But I wasn't prepared for an editorial shift at *Superromance*. Promotions, transfers, firings—the type of personnel changes that happen at any company were now directly affecting me. Authors have no say in these management decisions. We're recipients of change and have to adjust to the new editorial team while team members get to know their authors. Inadvertently, I had more down time than I wanted.

A proposed trilogy became a one-book offering, *A Man of Honor*, published in 2006. I submitted more proposals for stories and slowly received a contract here and there. Then came the exciting news about a new line opening up the next year: *Everlasting Love*. These would be stories of long-term relationships, of exploring the *happily ever after* over many years. My proposal for a love story set in WWII New York was accepted, and I was happy again on the writing front.

In the meantime, Rick and Sandy asked us to go house hunting with them in Connecticut. They'd moved to their own apartment after the wedding, but two years later, wanted to take the next step and become homeowners. Mike and I were thrilled to be so trusted. We'd planned to visit both grandmas in New York anyway, so on a rainy day in April, we joined the kids and began what turned out to be a successful search.

Several months later, after announcing they were pregnant, the young couple moved into their new home. Naturally, Blanche and Dee wanted to visit and be part of the excitement. My mom was eighty-nine by then, and struggling more than ever. Dee, at eighty-eight, was amazingly fit.

We brought the ladies to the house, Blanche's wheelchair and walker in the trunk of our car. Once at the front door, however, she had a three-step journey before she could rely on the walker for help. With Mike and I on either side of her, she climbed those stairs as though climbing Everest, every footstep placed just so. A nimble brain and a failing body. It broke my heart, especially knowing that a slow-growing cancer had established residence near her bile ducts.

A month after that visit, we celebrated my mom's ninetieth birthday at the annual get-together of my dad's family. My cousin Randy hosted the clan and provided the birthday girl with a gold crown for the occasion. Mom loved it and sat at the head of the table surrounded by her subjects, laughing, joking and catching up on family events.

I took a mental snapshot of my smiling mother in her crown before I reached for the camera. Once embedded in my mind, I can carry the picture with me always.

CHAPTER EIGHTEEN

ENDINGS AND BEGINNINGS

New York
February 2007

If it seems as if I kept the airlines in business with my flights to New York, I did. My sister kept me up-to-date about our mother's condition, and I took long weekends to fly north. In early 2007, I didn't buy a return ticket. Slow-growing or not, the cancer had taken its toll, turning Mom's stomach rock hard. Judy and I stayed with her as much as possible in the hospital and later, when she received hospice treatment, at a nursing home.

I was not strong then. I kissed her, stroked her, and provided her with ice chips. But I couldn't prevent tears from welling.

"Don't be sad," she said, as my eyes filled up yet again. She trailed her fingers in the air an inch above the sheet and whispered, "Acceptance, acceptance."

Did I have another choice?

For her sake, I tried to blink my eyes dry, but my heart ached without pause. My champion lay dying. The one person who'd loved me without condition or restraint. The person who raised me to follow my own path as she'd followed hers. She devoured mystery novels, had never read a romance in her life. And yet, she was so proud of me—her new favorite author.

I knew pain lodged everywhere in her body, but no narcotics for her; she wanted a clear mind. She wanted to…know. And besides, narcotics always made her nauseous.

"Ma," I said, "it hurts to see you so weak."

She raised her arm, curled her fingers into the semblance of a fist. "But I was strong when I needed to be strong!"

Of course she'd been strong—for her entire life as a wife, mother, career woman, beloved aunt, friend and mahjong champ. And in her youth, nursing her own dying mother, slipping ice chips into that lady's mouth. I am sixty and can barely manage. How could she have borne it?

She turned her head on the pillow and looked at me straight on.

"You'll never forget this time," she whispered, and I knew she was thinking of her own mother, my grandmother, whom I'd never met.

"I love you, Ma."

"And I love you."

She succumbed a few days later, on February 25, 2007, but death did not win.

Exactly a month later, on March 26th, Sandy and Rick became parents of a baby girl and named their daughter after her great-grandma. While the candle may flicker and dim, it does not go out. Grandma Blanche lives on through me and my children and my children's children.

In the end, love always triumphs.

Love has no ending. It is what sustains us.

My grandmother Annie immigrated to the U.S. from Poland in about 1910 and carried the BCRA1 gene.

October 2001, four months after the end of chemo at the
Ninc conference at St. Pete's Beach, FL

It takes awhile for hair to grow in nicely. Personally, I don't look good in very short hair, so I stuck with the wig for awhile.

Mike and I on New Year's Eve in Florida, four weeks after my implant was removed in Tampa. The jacket hides a lot of improvisation!

A little older and wiser. Still happy!

CHAPTER NINETEEN

RETIREMENT: ONE SIZE DOESN'T FIT ALL

At the end of 2007, Mike decided to retire. He'd been working since he was twelve years old, when he delivered orders for a local fruit and vegetable store after school. He'd lived in the Midwood section of Brooklyn at that time, and in those days, a penny was dear. He'd wanted his own pennies.

He worked his way through all kinds of kid jobs, from delivery boy to dishwasher in a Chinese restaurant, to waiter, to supermarket stock clerk and checkout person, to hotel wait staff. Earning his own way became a habit as he grew from boy to man. A couple of college diplomas in psychology enabled him to start his professional business career in the Human Resources area. His diverse responsibilities ensured he was never bored during the first eighteen years of his career while we lived in New England.

Just as in other aspects of life, however, change

arrives. Our move to Houston had been part of that change. Two years later, a broken promise. The job disappeared. He found something else, and we adjusted. But then another short-lived promise reared its head. He kept at the job search, never gave up. And found another position. But by the summer of 2007, he derived no satisfaction from working at all. Computing some numbers told us we'd be all right financially if he retired, including the cost of health benefits.

Then I had a brilliant thought. Why not both of us retire? The adult education program at my agency had changed dramatically. Instead of working with a full class of students aimed at high school equivalency, instead of using platform skills and group coaching, my classroom had become a study hall. I worked one-on-one with the three or four individual students who showed up, and who could barely read or write. We were mismatched. These students deserved a teacher who specialized in teaching on the most basic of literacy levels. My strengths lay elsewhere. And on top of that, my wonderful friend and boss, Kate, had accepted a position at another company.

I made my pitch. "Mike, just think. I'd be able to write full-time. Maybe I'll earn more than I do now. I'd love to try it...and besides, retirement will be more fun if we do it together—except, of course, I really won't be retired."

His eyes lit up. "Can't turn down fun, can we?"

"And that includes more opportunities to see the kids! Our time would be flexible."

With the babies living over a thousand miles away from me in two different states, I worried that they'd never bond with their grandpa or me. Mike and I sometimes felt like jet setters, never taking a real vacation, but using those funds for trips to each son's house twice a year. My first granddaughter, who was four-and-a-half, had seen us no more than ten times, and that included when she was born! It wasn't enough. It wasn't how I imagined my life as a grandma.

I'd dreamed of Sunday afternoon dinners at my house. I'd dreamed of cuddling on the couch and reading stories together or going to the park together. I'd dreamed of spur-of-the-moment times when we could whip up some chocolate pudding in my kitchen. I'd dreamed of riding bikes with them and watching soccer games on a Tuesday evening.

I know I'm not the only grandma who loves from afar. Or who orders pictures over the Internet as soon as my daughters-in-law post new albums to my inbox. Or who has covered her refrigerator from corner to corner with photos of the children. In today's world, families go where the jobs are. Mike and I did the same by moving to Massachusetts and then to Texas. I understand about earning a living and supporting a family. But it doesn't mean I have to like the fallout. Thinking about it still breaks my heart to this day.

The decision to leave my day job offered such temptation, but was also so scary that I blogged about it:

A WEEKEND WRITER NO MORE –

Two days ago, I submitted a letter of resignation at my day job. I say it's time. My writing friends say it's about time.

After fifteen years of working in education and employment programs with disadvantaged clients, the last seven of which also included a second job—writing novels for Harlequin—I had reached a crossroad. It's not because I wanted to tell my employer to "take this job and shove it." In fact, I've derived immense satisfaction from assisting people to earn their GED diplomas, construct resumes for their job search, and provide food from our pantry when they needed sustenance.

I have enjoyed the camaraderie of co-workers whose goals were similar to mine. Lunchtime with some of my peers has resulted in good friendships. I have also enjoyed receiving a paycheck every week! Writers are self-employed with income arriving sporadically.

I will miss the day job; I do not leave it lightly. But time is passing.

I know I am fortunate to have tasted success as a novelist. The pleasure of connecting with readers who write to me about my stories, the author friends I've made and the joy I've had in delving deeply into the craft itself cannot be overstated. I've loved it all! And I want to taste a full-time writing career. Are there stories I might imagine if I had more time to dream, or to conduct research? Do I have the skills to flex more writing muscle? Frankly, I don't know. But I want to find out. And time is passing.

I have already lived the dreams of every little girl—falling in love, becoming a young wife, a new mother, an equal partner in a wonderful marriage. I count my blessings every single day. And although time is passing, there is a season for everything. This is my season for a new dream.

I wish you many seasons and many dreams.
Linda, posted 11/20/07

#

Never-ending Adjustments

Mike and I agreed to continue living in Houston. We'd made friends, established a happy social life, and just as important, I had my writing support groups. By far, however, the definite factor was that our middle son, David—and his rescue dog—lived nearby. Sure, Dave was still single and on his own, but that didn't make him any less important than his brothers. Mike and I had always thought we'd go to Florida when the time was right because of Andy, Pauline and the kids. But we wouldn't leave David alone without family nearby. So, we settled into new routines in our familiar setting. And the chorus among our working friends sounded like this:

"How's retired life?"

"You're so lucky to be out of the rat race."

"Getting on each others' nerves yet?"

"Are you going to take up golf and hit the links with Mike?"

I have to admit that for a little while, my identity with Mike seemed to blur. I began to think I was retired, too, in a weird sort of way. Sure, I was still writing, but my seven-year strict commuter work schedule was gone. Suddenly, my time was flexible—something I'd wanted very much. However, the intoxicating freedom confused me. I was finally able to write full-time from home, but now I was squeezing that work in between other life activities. Was there something wrong with this picture? What had I done? In a little while, I realized that every change—even a positive one—requires an adjustment period.

Writers sometimes talk about the "birthing" of a book. We labor over a novel, giving it our blood, sweat and tears, riding the emotional roller-coaster with our characters for nine months or so, and *voila*! We give birth to a book. My tenth romance, *Houseful of Strangers,* was published in March, the same month as my second granddaughter's birth. *HoS* was a good story—received great reviews—but it did not generate the excitement that a beautiful, healthy flesh-and-blood, sweet, live baby did. Which serves to remind us that metaphors are simply metaphors. Nothing beats the real thing.

At the end of 2007 came the publication of my eleventh book, *The Soldier and the Rose,* part of *Harlequin's Everlasting Love* series. The reality of authoring eleven books made me pause. Every one of them had been a challenge to write. I'd sweated the ideas and worried about the characters. I'd worried about the plots, too. What should happen next? Words, words, words. I needed words put together in just the right way for readers to care about my characters. Readers want to ride an emotional wave. Smooth prose alone doesn't work. If it doesn't touch the emotions, it might as well not be written.

Every once in a while, however, a story comes along that almost writes itself. *The Soldier and the Rose* was that story for me. Like a waterfall from which I was the source, words poured and ideas came so quickly, instinctively, that I knew this story had been sitting inside my heart for a long time. A story of family. A story of everlasting love. An idea that had sprung from my father-in-law's wartime correspondence.

This novel saluted the WWII generation, but was specifically a valentine to my own family's history, typical of the immigrant Jewish experience in Brooklyn, New York. Immediately, I had the setting. Not only could I picture the setting—a street lined with brownstone houses and stoops—but I smelled the aromas of the neighborhood, the chicken soup, pot roast, and the rugulahs filled with sugar, cinnamon and raisins. In my mind's eye, I saw the pompadour hairstyles and long dresses from the era. I recalled the sense of community as my mom, aunts and uncle talked about their young lives through the years of the Great Depression and the war. I'd been born in that neighborhood, too, and had my own little girl memories.

I loved writing this novel, loved bringing to life the sensibilities of those times. When my mom was ill, I told her the story, told her that the characters were based on her and her sisters and brother. Several times, she asked, "What happens next?" So, I knew either the story had some heft or she liked hearing about "the old days."

That valentine to my family had been a one-book contract and was completed the same year Mike and I retired, and I began writing from home. Happily, I'd just signed another contract for two more stories with a new editor. I had plenty to keep me busy and could proclaim my status as a full-time writer without lying to anyone, including myself.

Shortly thereafter, however, changes loomed on the writing front—changes to the story length and to the editorial staff. It now took months to hear whether proposals would be accepted or not. The new editor who'd contracted the two books with me didn't like my other ideas. Three proposals were rejected on the same day. Later, I had to rewrite about fifty percent of the first manuscript I'd submitted to fulfill that contract. So, I guess she didn't like my writing either. I delivered the second complete manuscript in September 2008 and kept submitting more proposals. When my editor called me at home some weeks later, she told me how much she disliked the completed manuscript, and I had to rewrite the entire story from Page One. Obviously, we were not a match made in Heaven.

Fortunately for my disheveled ego, 2009 and 2010 brought some good news as *Summer at the Lake* won awards, and *Quarterback Daddy* became a reader favorite. Regardless of that happy result, I had no new contracts, nothing else in the hopper. Maybe I shouldn't have left my day job.

Or maybe it was time to spread my writing wings.

#

Making a Move

By the time 2008 ended, I'd been cancer free for over seven years. Of course, I continued with my mammograms every December and visited with Dr. B, but I wasn't overly nervous anymore. Mike and I fell into a new rhythm accented with my writing and critiquing with my writing buddies, his golf and volunteering on the course, exercising at the gym and socializing with friends. Phyllis had invited me to join her mahjong group on Fridays. I accepted and acquired two new friends, Gail and Lou (nickname for Linda).

One year later, in August 2009, Sandy and Rick presented us with another miracle: a precious grandson to love. In a short span of time, Mike and I had experienced the most poignant of life-cycle events—marriages, births, and deaths. Through them all, my emotions flowed and overflowed. If my cancer had killed me, I would have missed knowing these beautiful children. They would have missed hugs and kisses from a loving grandma. I was so thankful to be alive. Thankful for being lucky.

The surprises weren't over. A year later, in October 2010, after Mike and I returned from the wonderful—and revealing—Novelists, Inc. conference called *Brainstorming on the Beach* where our eyes were opened to the changes starting to occur in publishing, our son David had an announcement. No, not a marriage, but a move. He'd accepted a job in Oklahoma. He quickly contacted a Realtor and listed his house for sale. We helped him load the pick-up truck, and off he went with Abby, his sweet ninety-three pound mixed-breed rescue dog.

David's relocation acted as our signal to rethink a move to Florida. Yes, we were happy in the Lone Star State, but we had kids and grandkids in the Sunshine

State, and that is a draw that can not be overlooked. I had also noted earlier that Tampa is home to the Moffitt Cancer Center, arguably the leading cancer hospital in Florida. The thought of leaving Dr. B's care made my nerve endings raw, but I couldn't allow phantom worries and "what if's" to dictate my life. I'd survived for nine years now, and I had to think positive.

Naturally, we were aware that Florida is the retirement capital of the United States. Or at least of the east coast. I went online to research possible communities and discovered Mike and I were *not* 55 and *older*; we were 55 and *better*. We were "active" seniors. Who knew?

After chatting with David to make sure his position in Tulsa was working out, Mike and I trekked to our son's house in Florida at the beginning of December 2010. With brochures in hand, we drove to Orlando and then to a couple of places closer to our son's house. We narrowed the search down to two communities and every day went back and forth, trying to decide between them.

How can you foresee where you'll be happiest? You can't. Both communities were lovely and offered similar amenities at a similar price. In the end, we based our choice on the house layout, picked out a lot and put down the required deposit. The house would be ready for us sometime in August or September 2011. Perfect timing. We'd have at least eight or nine months to prepare and place our Houston house on the market.

We returned home with mixed emotions, excited about our decision, but sad at the prospect of leaving so many friends and sweet memories. Sixteen years is not sixteen minutes. We'd already learned from our Massachusetts experience, however, that by picking up the phone (somehow email isn't the same), friendships can remain strong. But that didn't make the telling any easier.

With so many items on my To-Do list, I was distracted, but not so distracted that I forgot about my annual mammogram. Later that month, I drove to Dr. B's clinic and signed in at the Radiology department on the first floor.

"We need to take an extra film," said the tech afterwards as I waited in my cotton gown for permission to leave.

"How come?" I felt my chest tighten and perspiration gather in the nooks and crannies of my body.

"Oh, she just needs a clearer film."

Okay, no need to panic. The picture was simply blurry. That's happened before. No problem.

Relaxed again, I got dressed afterward, took the elevator Dr.B's office on the 4th floor, ready for my yearly check-up. He and Grace were waiting for me.

"We just got the call from downstairs," said Dr. Bernicker, his voice tight, his complexion pale.

And that's how I knew I'd stepped on another landmine.

CHAPTER TWENTY

AT THE WHEEL

Same breast. Slightly smaller tumor than the last one. And that's all we knew about the thing at that moment.

Could it be a recurrence after nine years? That thought made my head spin. Had one tiny cancer cell been hiding out in my body patiently waiting to attack? Or had a new enemy invaded? We'd been testing my blood regularly since my first bout for a specifically elevated blood protein, a breast cancer marker. The test is called the CA 125. If the blood had revealed it, we would have had a heads-up. My last test, however, had been negative.

Dr. B was going on about possibilities, making arrangements for an ultrasound, jabbering to Grace and me. I tried to pay attention, but inside I was shrieking, *I've got cancer again, I've got cancer again!* And then I did shriek out loud, "But I can't have Adria! What are we going to do?" I'd tucked the knowledge of the Red Devil's nasty cardio effects away in my brain, just in case. And now just-in-case was real.

"Don't worry about that," said Dr. B, sounding very nonchalant. "We've got other drugs which can do the job just as well."

Really?

"And I'm moving to Florida! Oh, my God. I don't believe this." The timing couldn't have been worse.

"When are you going?"

"Next August or September."

He waved his arm. "You'll be fine and ready. It'll all be over by then."

So maybe the timing could have been worse. What if the cancer had shown up in Florida where I had no team? Fortunately, Dr. B was at the wheel again, driving my bus.

"But now we need to talk about that test for the gene mutation," he said. "You're definitely a candidate—a second occurrence, Eastern-European Jewish ancestry, two cousins affected—so insurance should cover a chunk of it. The test is expensive."

I certainly wasn't rich, but at the moment, I wasn't concerned about money either. I just wanted to get rid of the damn tumor. My stomach twisted. Maybe my cousin Sheila had been right. I should have had the genetic test five years ago. I should have faced the truth then. Maybe I was a carrier of the BRCA1 or BRCA2 gene mutation. Maybe my cancer destiny had been pre-ordained genetically, and I'd waited too long to find out. Too long to change that destiny. I hated my Cleopatra persona. Being Queen of De-nial translated to being Queen of Stupidity.

"So, what's the plan?" I asked, my voice shaking. I had high expectations for a man who had barely been given time to absorb the news himself.

"We need more information," said Dr. B. "First, you're going to have an ultrasound guided biopsy. I'm sending you to the best radiological surgeon in the city. He specializes in breast tissue. You can have it done at St. Luke's or Methodist. Do you have a preference?"

"Maybe it's not cancer," I said, ignoring his question. "Maybe it's just a-a-calcification or something."

Dr. B stared at me for a long moment before quietly agreeing. "Maybe."

And maybe I had a screw loose somewhere. I didn't care. I wanted a possibility of salvation, even if it were no more than a five percent chance.

Despite the sunny, cool weather, my hands perspired on the wheel as I drove home across the city on the interstate. Watch the right lane. Check the rearview mirror. Pay attention ahead. The guy on the left wants to pass. What exit is this? Get to the right. Signal for lane change. Every automatic response of an experienced driver became a conscious choice. Maybe we turn to the mundane to get us through the nightmares. Watching traffic kept me sane. It prevented me from screaming Mike's name.

Michael. Oh, my dear Michael. My devoted Knight. Another battle loomed, and his tinfoil would need polishing again. So unfair. My tears dropped onto the steering wheel, and I struggled to see the road ahead.

CHAPTER TWENTY ONE

HORROR AND HOPE

"We'll get you through this again. I'm not going to let you die." From Mike's mouth to God's ears. My darling thought he could control the world. I knew better, but I wanted to believe him—had to believe him—to keep myself sane.

The mammo had shown the cyst to be smaller than the first one, but I'd been stirred and shaken harder than Bond's martini and couldn't concentrate on anything other than the ultrasound appointment scheduled for the following week, that holiday stretch between Christmas and New Year's. Dr. B must have pulled strings at St. Luke's. Who gets a last minute appointment during Christmas week with the highest-ranking radiological breast surgeon at the Houston medical center? Either Dr. B had a lot of clout or the mission of the hospital was to move Heaven and Earth for the sake of the patient. I actually hoped it was the latter but wasn't questioning this good fortune.

Once more, Mike and I kept the news to ourselves,

not because we were martyrs, but because we had nothing much to say yet. We had no hard pieces of information to share, no treatment plan either, so we'd not be able to answer the thousand questions that would surely come our way. Besides, why make everyone miserable with the wait?

Slowly, very slowly, one day followed another. Had I been working a regular job, I might have been distracted. But, then again, maybe not. I tried to write. I was working on a women's fiction novel and would consider self-publishing this time. That's what I learned about at the brainstorming conference on St. Pete's Beach. Due to the advent of electronic publishing and the availability of Kindles, Nooks and a host of electronic readers, authors had options other than the traditional publishing route. So, while waiting for my ultrasound appointment, I kept myself busy, but the waiting was hard. I still kept hoping for the best—a tiny little nodule that could be cut out. Something so small, I wouldn't need chemo. In this situation, you don't have to be a professional author to imagine your own happy script.

On December 29, 2010, I finally met Dr. H, the Master of the Breast Ultrasound. A kind man with a loud machine. With a procedure called an image-guided ultrasound biopsy, the goals were to locate the cyst and take samples to see what we were truly dealing with. Had my prior cancer somehow returned after nine whole years? Was this something new? The only fact we had at this point was an approximate size of the tumor.

Next to the table where I lay stood the ultrasound scanner. It contained a computer, a video display screen, and a cord with a probe at the end, which looked like a microphone—with a needle. Dr. H held the probe in his hand and started his exploration into the mass. Click, click, bang, bang! On and on.

It's all about sonar. High frequency sound waves that we can't hear go out, and returning sonar echoes come back. We hear those! The machine measures them, determining location, size, etc. It's similar to sonar used by boats and submarines. The test lasted about forty minutes, enough time for Mike to have gone to his dental appointment and return.

I was alone, but in good hands, when Dr. H. put his instruments away, and with kindness in his eyes and voice, confirmed what we'd already known.

"Yes, this is cancer."

I thought I'd been prepared, so why did tears roll down my temples onto the table where I lay? "But I have grandchildren!" I protested. "They need me. I need them. A *bat mitzvah* in ten years…"

Then Dr. H uttered the one sentence that kept me sane—and continues to do so—at least most of the time. He said, and I quote, "This will not kill you."

This will not kill you. This will not kill you. I glommed onto his pronouncement.

"You'll be at the party."

Breathing became easier. "So…another lumpectomy?"

The man remained perfectly still, eyes softening further as he waited for me to connect the dots.

"Mastectomy?" I whispered.

The silence deepened throughout the small room. Neither of us moved. Dr. H stared at me, *willing* me to take it one step further.

"A double?" My lips barely moved as I shivered in my gown.

Finally he nodded, a bob of his head. "Physically, we could do a lumpectomy, but what will you have left? It's the same breast, and, more important, this is your second cancer…" His voice trailed off, once more, allowing me to reach the logical conclusion. Did I want to risk a third time, a fourth time?

Hell, no! Not when he'd already told me I'd be okay. Now I understood he also meant, *if you take the right precautions.*

With compassion and kindness, Dr. H managed to deliver some tough medical truths. He and I were together just this one time—a short time—but I will never forget his humanity. No wonder Dr. Bernicker felt confident sending me to this specialist. I was only one of several patients that day, and each day brings Dr. H more women in crisis. More tests and prognoses. I believe he's a courageous man, and perhaps unique for a surgeon, to allow emotions inside the examining room.

In the car going home, I said to Mike, "I've made my decision. I'm having a double mastectomy."

"Probably," he said. "Ninety-five percent or higher chance. But let's wait for Dr. B's opinion."

The ball would now be thrown into Dr. B's court. After receiving the pathology results of this biopsy, we would discuss options, but in the end, he would chart a course for me to follow. Despite kindnesses from all the medical folks cheering me on, I knew the road ahead would be rougher than it should have been because of our relocation to Florida. Between my illness and a long distance move, albeit for a positive reason, we were about to tackle two of the top five stressors people face in their lives. And we'd be dealing with them simultaneously.

The first time I had cancer, I vowed it would not take over my life, but be only a part of it. I saw no reason to think any differently now. Sure, I was scared. I was scared witless. But, if I loosened the reins on the fear and the disease, I knew they would consume me. What would my life be worth then?

CHAPTER TWENTY TWO

APPOINTMENTS!
APPOINTMENTS!
APPOINTMENTS!

Mike and I needed two calendars as we headed into 2011. One for the Realtor and all things house-related, the other for doctors and all things medically-related. As for writing, I was challenging myself to branch out into larger stories of family drama—more layered plots and characters—with romance as part of it, but not the main story line. I wanted to change gears, but it wasn't easy. Heck, it's never easy to write any good book, whatever the length and subject; it's never easy to create something out of nothing. Which is why a good read gets noticed. Despite the difficulties, I needed to spread my wings and figure it out. My philosophy was the same as when I'd left the day job three years before: If not now, when?

I also thought Murphy's law had reignited itself. Why did everything go wrong at the same time? For a while, I thought it was only me. Like a teenager, I was sure the spotlight was always on me, right? But of course, my reasoning was faulty. Murphy wouldn't have become a law if lots of other people weren't going through lots of stinking craziness as well.

A few days after the ultrasound, my blood was drawn at Dr. B's office. It would be sent to, what was at that time, the only lab in the country performing the test for mutated breast and ovarian genes. These genes are found in several ethnic groups but none with as high a frequency as my group—Jewish people of Eastern European ancestry. The lab's standard waiting time was two weeks; they'd fax the results directly to Dr. B.

In the meantime, we talked. A lot. In his office. What if I wasn't a carrier of the gene mutation? Would I still want bilateral surgery? This was why Mike had held out at a 95% probability rate. He wanted the lab results first before making the 100% commitment. Not that it was *his* final choice. As for me, I thought the girls should go because, as I said at the time, "I'm not going through chemo again after this!" I was upset enough about facing it for a second time. I couldn't fathom a third time or more.

As for Dr. B, his opinion was not kept secret: bilateral mastectomy. "Even if you don't have the gene mutation, you've already had breast cancer twice. Why take another chance? In the end, it's your decision, Linda, but if you were my wife, it's the double."

What about a single? If I had only a single mastectomy, would that resolve anything? I had to think about that. It didn't take long. I'd probably want a mammo every month to make sure the remaining breast was clean. So, I wouldn't be relaxed; it would be on my mind all the time.

With a double, I'd be giving up a healthy breast. I glanced down at my one healthy boob and one sick boob. Both had well-functioning nipples, and crap, I'd miss them. So would Mike. The girls fit nicely into a 34C bra. They looked pretty good in blouses and sweaters head-on or in profile. More important, they were mine. Part of me. My whole life. I knew them. Was used to them. Liked them. They'd nursed my youngest baby.

But now, they were killing me. Literally.

Amputate.

"So-so what happens afterward?" I whispered.

"You've got choices," said Dr. B. "But you're young, fit, like to dress nicely—"

Nicely? He never saw me in my old raggedy jeans that I wore every day at the computer.

"—I'd suggest implants."

Implants. Another topic to explore.

"Of course, not everyone chooses them," Dr. B continued, "and there's nothing wrong with wearing prosthetic bras instead." He stared at me. "But you know, I see a lot of women who've chosen to go that route, and frankly, they're always adjusting themselves and their clothes. They look okay, but they don't seem able to forget about checking their appearance. I think you'd be happier with implants."

I held up my hand. "You know what? My head's exploding. TMI for one day." I needed time to digest what probably lay before me. Major surgeries. Pain. Implants. I had a strong hunch these implants were not the same as those chased by Hollywood.

"My office will call you with dates for your MRI and for your appointment with the general surgeon." He grinned. "You'll like her. She's got personality and superb skills."

I didn't care about personality, have never judged a physician on bedside manner, especially a surgeon. For that specialty, I wanted hands of gold.

#

Getting the Word Out

Email is a wonderful way to communicate with people important to you and who care about you. I decided to break the news to my peeps through the Internet instead of making the many phone calls it would require. On January 5, 2011, this is part of what I wrote:

Subject: Once more, into the brink...

Dear all,

I really don't know how to break this gently, except to say that I have a new breast cancer (same breast as last time) that must be treated. I've been biopsied and diagnosed, but am still waiting for more information before we can determine the correct course to follow.

I'm being tested for the BRCA1 & 2 genes. If I'm a carrier, then a double mastectomy and excision of ovaries will be done. If I'm not a carrier, then I can choose a single or double. Chemo is also a possibility depending on the make-up of the tumor (still waiting for that info).

I've been down this road before and it sucks.

BUT THE GOOD NEWS IS: I WILL LIVE TO DANCE AT MY GRANDDAUGHTER'S BAT MITZVAH, which is ten years down the road!

This will be cured just like my last one, which was nine years ago, and is totally unrelated to the current cancer. That's also good news. My lymph node was negative, too, but more lymph nodes will be tested at the time of the surgery.

Maybe this is TMI. Sorry, if so.

I continue to write fiction. Writing is therapy. Still trying to get to FB on a regular basis. I seem to do it in spurts. And, we're committed to moving to Florida in August or September. We've already contracted for a house. So, as usual, life "gets in the way" of our best-laid plans. However, Winston Churchill said, "Never, never, never give up." Considering he was a pretty tough dude, I'll follow his advice again.

I know you'll be rooting for me, and that helps.

Love, Linda, who's planning to attend the Ninc writing conference in October.

#

Life in Small Boxes—
Don't Forget the Realtor's Appointment

I've never had a great memory, so I kept one calendar at my kitchen desk and one in my purse. They were identical and necessary to keep myself organized. With a load of appointments exacerbated by a load of stress, I not only forgot details but important things too. I began writing everything down. My life was outlined in little boxes.

This is the schedule I kept the week after seeing Dr. B:

Monday: Realtor, 10 a.m.

Tuesday: MRI, St. Luke's, 2:15 p.m., 10th Floor; wait for films if hospital says it's possible; bring them to surgeon

Wednesday: Mike at Dentist, 8:15 a.m.

Thursday: Dr. GZ, general surgeon, 10:15 a.m.

Friday: Dr. B, Noon; to discuss all findings and get his input; BRCA results??

Friday: Phyllis & Jeff: 6 p.m. Rehearsal dinner for Brad and Cully.

Saturday night: Wedding

Amid the angst, great joy beckoned at the marriage of my friends' son and lovely future daughter-in-law. We'd looked forward to this celebration for a year, and Mike and I were determined to kick back and raise our glass of champagne with everyone else. No matter what. Even if I was too nervous to eat dinner. Worry and joy mixing it up—isn't that what life is about? Does anyone have it all good or all bad? On the night of the wedding, Phyllis ran a 102-degree temp. She pasted a smile on her face and looked beautiful as she played the hostess with a strength of will to be admired. She collapsed later.

Studying my new bible—the calendar—and imagining what laid ahead stressed me to the point of focusing on only one day at a time. One hour at a time. It seemed I'd figured out how to live in the moment, not think about tomorrow because the present was all I could handle.

It sounds trivial. All my life, I'd heard people advise taking one thing at a time, living in the day. I'd never been that kind of a person. Planning ahead is more my style. Being prepared. Figuring things out before needing them. I know it's about control. If I could control my world, I could keep everyone I loved safe. What a joke.

To get through the next few months, I'd need to be flexible. The old phrase of rolling with the punches applied. The comforting Serenity Prayer kicked around in my mind, helping me to reach some level of calmness. I recalled it again after the visit from the Realtor.

April came to the house on Monday. A young mother with high energy, the wife of my son's friend. She knew her stuff, and house-talk provided a great distraction from cancer. It also shocked us with additional expenses and work we'd have to do. Buyers were in the driver's seat in 2011, no doubt about that. They wanted everything updated, new and contemporary. Our to-do list included tearing down wallpaper, updating the kitchen, painting walls, repairing roof shingles, cleaning the carpet or replace it with wood flooring. Worst of all, our yard backed up to a street that had grown from two to four lanes. *Oy.*

"So does every house hunter think they're on HGTV or something?" I asked.

"Yup. They sure do."

"But that's crazy! I love the show, but man, sometimes I could wring their necks when they complain about nothing."

"Doesn't matter. It's their money and their choice."

"And we've got a lot of competition," said Mike, reviewing the comp lists April had brought with her. I peeked over his shoulder and agreed with him. The Realtor had done her research.

We talked money. She set up a date to send her photographer who would prepare a portfolio and a video to show off the house. Then we talked about a listing date.

"Whatever will work for you," said April. "We'll work around your schedule."

"I don't even have a surgery date yet." And then chemo—again. And getting rid of the accumulated junk in the house. And keeping the place spotless. And being nauseous, and—and—and how was I going to handle all this? My stomach churned and tightened. I could taste my own fear.

God grant me the serenity… Craig's voice popped into my head. My friend Craig had been the one who turned me onto this little prayer during my first bout with cancer when he, Kate and I lunched together. During the last three years, we still met at Niko's every few weeks, and now Craig's advice echoed again.

Just as my students had opened their hearts and gifted me with their prayers years ago, so had strangers by adding me to their prayer chains and prayer groups in church and online. I knew nothing about these activities until a co-worker mentioned his wife had added my name, and then someone else told me the same thing. I learned that illness makes us all brothers and sisters whatever our personal background. In our common humanity, I could accept prayers that didn't sound familiar to my ears. I could return the gift and offer my own traditional prayer—in Hebrew it's called the *Mi Shebeirach*—which includes healing of body, mind and spirit. I could offer it to those of any faith in need of healing and peace.

Cancer sucks. It blindsides us, indiscriminate in its victims. Craig needed those prayers himself during this time. Leukemia found him. He needed a bone marrow transplant and suffered weeks of nausea, vomiting and long stays in the hospital. A complicated recuperation. Thankfully, he survived. In those days, Kate's glances roved between Craig and me; she didn't know who to hug first. But that didn't stop her from speaking her mind.

"Maybe you shouldn't leave Houston."

"Good point. Think about that," Craig added.

"But who's the boss?" I asked. "Cancer or me?" Ten years ago, I'd vowed that the disease would not define me. I still felt the same. Besides, we'd already put down thousands of dollars on the new place—near my grandkids! That goal hadn't changed, so I kissed them both and gave them an open invitation to visit us in Florida. If we ever sold the house.

#

"It's January now, so if we list it in March," I said to April, "that gives us six months to sell. The new house should be ready in September. I'm going to need some healing time in the next few weeks anyway, so March should work."

"Now, in case the new house isn't ready," said April, "and we sell this one, you've got to be prepared to put things into storage."

And so it went. The endless possibilities of this or that happening—just in case, just in case—had me putting up my hands. "I'll worry about that later. What comes first?"

It came down to cleaning out stuff, repairing and renovating what needed to be done, and being ready to "stage" the place. Buyers wanted mint condition. Move-in ready plus, plus, plus. No envisioning the "potential" of a home. The potential had to be the reality. My translation: They didn't want to do any work themselves. Wouldn't that mean we could jack up the price? No, no, no. Not in this horrible housing market.

I turned to Mike. "We're starring in our own reality show called, *The Barretts Break Even—If Lucky*. Houses are supposed to be an investment. I don't like this, not after sixteen years. We have a beautiful home here, and I'm not giving it away."

Can you hear the echo of thousands of homeowners getting ready to sell?

As it turned out, I should have "given it away." I really didn't understand that the housing market was largely out of my control. In some parts of the country, real estate was in ruins. In Houston, not so much. But the rules of buying and selling had changed, and I didn't want to adapt. I just wanted to play fair by the old rules. Sometimes, I'm a slow learner.

CHAPTER TWENTY THREE

EEENY, MEENY, MINY, MO....

Who knew MRIs could be so loud, even louder than the ultrasound had been? MRI stands for Magnetic Resonance Imaging, and a breast MRI is given to people with high risk for breast cancer. So, there I was, in a cotton gown, lying face down on a padded table with my boobs hanging into hollow depressions. The entire table and I went through a narrow tunnel as the machine captured multiple pictures of my breasts. Detailed pictures of what was going on inside. I was told to lie still, which wasn't too hard after I got used to all the thumping and popping noises. No one else was in the room with me, but I could talk to a tech who was outside with a microphone. It lasted about thirty minutes. The staff was terrific. I wasn't scared, but I was glad when it was over.

On Thursday, I met the general surgeon, Dr. GZ. Blonde, slender, energetic and friendly, she was more experienced than she looked. She reassured me about her job—removing as much breast tissue as possible, which requires scraping the skin—to reduce the chance of cancer returning. We didn't want to offer the cancer any perch on which to attach itself. I loved when she said I had to make the choice that felt right for me. So, what were my choices?

After a mastectomy, I could choose to do nothing. Go flat. Many people go that route and have no regrets. They want the damn cancer out. Recovery is quicker. They want to proclaim, "This is who I am." The people in their lives love them; they are more than a breast. There's nothing wrong with going flat and natural.

The second choice was having implant reconstruction right there in the operating room immediately after the breasts were removed. This would require a plastic surgeon being in the OR at the same time as the general surgeon. This choice was a very popular one since a woman would wake from surgery with small breasts already there. They'd be filled with saline over the next few months, allowing the skin to stretch gradually. The technology was excellent, and in the end, another surgery would occur to exchange these expanders for the real implants. At that time, a tattoo of nipples and aureole would be the final touch to make the breasts look as normal as possible.

The third choice was to have the mastectomies and postpone the reconstruction for a future time. Some women needed more time to figure out what they want to do. Medically, it's no problem to postpone as long as the doctors know your intention beforehand so they could leave enough skin for later use. This is called skin-sparing surgery.

There were other reconstruction options, all requiring incisions in other places—abdomen, back, or buttocks. The abdomen surgery is attractive to some because it provides a little tummy tuck. But for every advantage there's a disadvantage. All in all, there was a lot of information requiring lots of research. I will say that the thought of extra incisions and moving body fat and muscle around didn't appeal to me. If I'd reconstruct, it would be with implants.

However, I didn't know what to do. My conflict could be easily described as fear of pain vs. fear of looking awful. I had to face facts. I was a woman who liked to look good. I didn't shop in Lord & Taylor. I shopped in Marshalls, but I knew what looked good on me and what didn't. I remember Dr. B's words about patients who kept adjusting their clothes, never totally secure in how they looked.

On the other hand, who needed possible complications like the chance of infection with an implant? Without reconstruction, any returning cancer could be more easily detected. Returning? I'd been reassured that there was a scant chance—less than one percent—after the breasts and ovaries are removed. After two hits, however, the chance of a third cancer is not something I could simply brush aside.

And then Dr. GZ patted me on the knee. "You're young, you're pretty…think about the implants."

"Young?" I said. "I'm a grandmother!"

"So what?" she replied instantly. "I've operated on women in their seventies who wanted the reconstructive surgery. And you? You're younger than your years. That's what I see."

I remained silent.

"You don't have to make up your mind now," she said. "You can postpone any plastic surgery for whenever you want it—even ten years down the road. If we do skin-sparing surgery, you'd be good at any time."

As usual, I had a lot to think about. There was a part of me who couldn't believe that I, Linda Barrett, was living out every woman's nightmare. In that twilight time before the surgery date, I lived in my own world, nodding and smiling at people, simply going through the motions, but not comprehending their words at all. At other times, I was fired up and couldn't wait to grab the enemy and beat him to death. Let's get on with it! Let's get it over with.

Should I choose reconstruction? Should I have a single or double? Until I had the result of the genetic test, I wasn't one hundred percent sure of the bilateral option. The difference between a single or double mastectomy would be significant later on. I didn't want to make a mistake.

Before I left her office, the surgeon gave me the name of a plastic surgeon she'd worked with many times and could refer with confidence. I took the card and slipped it into my wallet. Two surgeons. Everyone was a specialist.

"Yeah," said Mike. "One for the left side and one for the right."

Very funny. Leno and Letterman had nothing to worry about.

#

Once Again, Proving Knowledge is Power

Twenty-four hours later, Mike and I sat in Dr. B's office going over the results of the MRI and Ultrasound. The size of this tumor measured 1.4 centimeters. Chemo was definitely on the agenda.

Suck it up, Linda; suck it up. You're alive. It'll keep you alive.

Not Adria, of course. My healthy heart was innocent in all this. It had a right to remain healthy. If the tumor had been less than one centimeter, we could have had a discussion on the pros and cons of chemo, the variations of statistics and so on. But that point was moot. My new cocktail would be a mix of Taxotere and Cytoxan. As for the nausea of the past, Dr. B assured me not to worry.

"We've come a long way since your last time. You'll get the anti-nausea medication first—intravenously—plus a prescription for pills you'll keep at home. Most patients don't have a nausea problem anymore."

Sounded good to me.

"And you'll take two steroid pills a day for two days after the infusion."

"That's new."

He nodded. "It helps. Also, on the day after, you'll return here for a Neulasta shot."

I reached for a pad and pencil. "What's that?"

"Neulasta helps fight infection. The chemo slows down the bone marrow's production of cells. Neulasta is used to stimulate a certain type of white blood cell that's needed for infection fighting."

More chemistry. I mentally shrugged. Shots were easy enough to handle, and knowing Mike, he'd want to drive me back and forth.

"Now let's talk surgery," said Dr. B.

"Again?"

"We need a plan before you see the surgeons again. It's a tough decision, but—"

"—But if I were your wife, you'd want them both off. So, I guess you don't think the third time's really a charm?" And I couldn't believe I'd said that.

I guess Dr. B couldn't believe it either, not according to the incredulous expression that crossed his face.

Before he could respond, a knock at the door preceded Grace's entrance. Grace, waving a paper in her hand.

"This was just faxed in." She handed the sheet to

Dr. B who glanced from it to me and nodded.

"Here's the explanation. You're a carrier. A deleterious BRCA1 gene." He turned to me, held my gaze with a no-nonsense air. "That about ends this discussion. You know what you have to do now, don't you?"

A rhetorical question. Of course, I knew, but I didn't have to like it. A bilateral mastectomy was the only way to go. My 95% probability had become 100%. Despite the prior weeks of discussion, preparation and trying to come to terms, my stomach churned. Another reality check.

Even the best-laid plans move in a zigzag line. Forward, back, sideways. Maybe this, maybe that, maybe something else. A new wrinkle, a new piece of information.

Mike broke in. "I'm now at one hundred percent. No more vacillating. We know everything we need to know. It's a double."

"So, this is it," I gasped, my voice hoarse. "It's decided."

"That's not all," said Dr. B. "You'll need a full hysterectomy as well. The BRCA1 mutation greatly increases your chance of ovarian cancer."

Somewhere in the back of my mind, I'd known this. But…"When? When does this happen?"

"After the chemo," said Dr. B, patting me on the arm. "First things first. You'll decide with your surgeon."

Six months from now would be the target date for removing my ovaries. As usual, Mike wrapped his arms around me. "It'll be all right. As long as you wind up healthy, what does it matter? We'll figure everything else out."

Dr. B nodded. "My office will let your surgeon know, and she'll take it from there."

"And I'll tell the plastic surgeon on Monday," I said. "But in the meantime, I'm taking these girls to a wedding tomorrow night." It would be the last time I'd dress up and be the real me. "Who knows," I added, trying to smile, "maybe in the end, I'll give Hollywood some competition."

We left the office, and I got into the car, thankful not to be driving this time. My body shook inside and out. "Damn, Mike. There's a shitload of stuff ahead of me. Mastectomies, chemo, oophorectomy, implants and a move to Florida. How am I going to do all this? I'm scared."

My Knight in Shining Tinfoil squeezed my hand. If he was scared, too, he wasn't saying.

#

What are these things called BRCA genes?

I understood the bits and pieces of genetic information thrown at me, but never quite got the whole picture. As usual, I had to slowly process anything related to science. So, I asked questions and studied articles and books, particularly one called *Confronting Hereditary Breast and Ovarian Cancer*, published by Johns Hopkins Press.

I learned that everyone has BRCA genes. You, me and the guy next door. That's not the problem. In fact, the role of these genes is to *suppress* tumors. So, they're the good guys. The problem occurs if there are mutations on these genes. Be assured that most cancers are not hereditary. The majority are random hits that occur from damage our genes acquired along the road of life. For example, with skin cancer, healthy skin cells are mutated by exposure to too much sun. Between five to ten percent of ALL breast cancers and about twelve percent of ovarian cancers, however, are caused by genetic mutations in the BRCA genes that people inherit from their parents.

The two genes most responsible for these mutations are called BRCA1 and BRCA2. They run in families such as mine and can be handed down from fathers as well as mothers. Although these mutations are found in all ethnic groups and races, they are most prevalent in people of Ashkenazi Jewish descent. In this group, one person in forty is a carrier as opposed to one in three hundred-fifty to five hundred in the general population. Way back in history, some of my ancestors developed defects in these genes and passed it down to their progeny, generation after generation. To this very day. And to me.

With the sophistication of medical research and technology, we now know on exactly which chromosome these BRCA1 and BRCA2 genes are located. More important, these genes can be identified for the mutations.

So, when I received the lab report saying BRCA1 – *deleterious,* I knew the reason for my breast cancers and could make an informed choice of how to proceed. It's news that not only can shake up your life, but can save your life.

It saved mine.

CHAPTER TWENTY FOUR

EXPANDERS, IMPLANTS, AND...BOOBLESS SEX?

Breast reconstruction offers more choices than a supermarket's cereal aisle. Implants or flaps? Saline or silicon? Size, shape, skin condition after radiation that I'd had ten years before. Our first conversation with the plastic surgeon focused on all of the above. At the end, he gave me a book to take home about risks, failures and statistics.

I refused to think about failures. My body had already failed me twice, and I couldn't afford an undisciplined mind. What if this happened? What if that? What if? What if? Instead I visualized success. I just wanted to fix the problem and move on. I zeroed in on that Hollywood ending, ignoring the potential for disappointment, and ignoring the small risk that these procedures wouldn't work out for me.

I chose to have implants rather than flap surgery, an arguably simpler surgery requiring less time in the operating room. However, two surgeries are required. First, expanders are placed behind the pectoral muscles and every week or two Dr. R would inject saline until we reached the correct size for me. That was the frustrating part. I wouldn't know in advance what I'd look like because the sizes weren't measured in conventional bra sizes of A, B, C and so on. The sizes were measured in projections from the chest wall outward.

Dr. R took pictures of my natural body, all angles. He took measurements. But in the end, he wouldn't know the final result until he was in the operating room months from now doing the exchange surgery, where he'd remove the expanders and insert the final implants. It was only then, when I was actually on the table, that he could determine the best fit for me.

Eight days remained until my breasts would be removed and the expanders inserted. Both surgeons would be in the OR at the same time. Dr. GZ, the general surgeon, would excise as much breast tissue as possible as well as another lymph node for fast biopsy. If cancer were present, she'd remove the next node down the line until she came to a clean one. When her part was over, Dr. R, the plastic surgeon, would insert the expanders and close the incisions.

#

Boobless Sex…Is It Possible?

Eight days. Eight days of freedom left. Eight days to indulge in mind-blowing sex and make memories or…

"We're going to practice having some titless sex," said Mike. "No button playing allowed. No breast stroking allowed. We're gonna make this work."

Oh, my guy had rules, and of course, I went along

with them. After all, I wanted to know the answers, too. Making love was not only a vital part of our marriage, but I believe it's a vital part of any happy marriage. I wasn't ready to give it up.

If ever two people were on a mission, we were. Make it work? Never had I realized exactly how erogenous a neck could be. The same for ear lobes. And mouth. And tongue. But, on the other hand, maybe I did. After all, I'd written a dozen romances, and the couples involved were all healthy. Yeah, Mike and I made it work—no boobs involved.

Maybe love works in crazy ways. And funny ways. Or maybe I was so much on edge that given half a chance, I was primed to release tension. Or maybe, the experimental foreplay gave us the illusion of controlling a horrible situation. Whatever the explanation, I knew we'd be all right in bed.

How else did we spend the week before surgery?

Cleaning the house. The nesting instinct coupled with meeting the target date of February 7th for getting the house on the market. I had no idea how we'd do all this, but I was determined to try. In the end, our MO of keeping busy worked again because suddenly, D-Day arrived, and on Tuesday, January 25th, Mike and I pulled up to the hospital at six a.m. At nine, I was wheeled into the OR.

Unknown to me, two friends stayed with Michael as he waited through the surgery. I slept through the dramatic interplay between Mike and Dr. GZ. It seemed she'd stepped into the waiting room with the results of the biopsy. No cancer in the first lymph node. Crying, my knight collapsed into her arms. A clean sentinel lymph node. Magical words, the elixir that fortified Mike's belief in our survival as a couple.

But when I awoke in the recovery room, wrapped in a special support bra with drains hanging from each side,

I knew none of this. All I knew was I couldn't move my arms. And that the clock was ticking. Mastectomy is considered day surgery. The twenty-four hours began the moment I hit the recovery room, but I couldn't imagine going home any time soon.

I should have imagined it. Twenty-three hours later I was home, wrapped in blankets on the couch, unable to move my arms. But there were two small bumps on my chest, the promise of things to come.

#

Getting the Word Out, Part Two

Three days after surgery, I emailed my friends and family:

Date: 1/28/2011
Subject: Home again, home again…yay!

Hi Y'all,
I'm still alive and intend to remain so. The good news—the best news—is that my lymph nodes under the arm were negative for cancer. When Mike heard this, he cried. Not only is this a relief that the cancer was contained, but also reduces or eliminates the chance that I'll wind up with lymphedema, a painful, swollen arm syndrome common after lymph node removal.

So, the bad girls are gone, and the good girls are slowly making an appearance. I've still got a long way to go, but honestly, I can only do it one day at a time or it's overwhelming. Today, I'm giving orders, being waited on, eating Sees chocolate and crocheting a lot. Obviously, I'm back on the computer, too.

I registered for the Ninc (Novelists, Inc.) conference yesterday. Registering filled a need to remain connected to the writing scene, because sometimes I feel I'm disappearing. So today, I will write at least two pages of my (new) work-in-progress. It's the only way I know to fight back.

I hope everyone is fine and doing whatever it is that makes you happy. Thanks for your good wishes, hugs and prayers. I'll still be counting on them as I continue this journey.

Love, Linda

#

On Your Mark, Get Set, Go!

I was hoping for a break. Just a couple of weeks to stay home and recoup. Get my strength back. Get rid of the drains. What was I thinking? Breast cancer rests for no one.

Six days post-op, I was at the plastic surgeon's office. He removed only one drain instead of two. Guess I'm slow about some things. A week later, I had my first "fill," and watched the girls expand. Of course, the more they expanded, the more it hurt. I tried to ignore that part.

During the same week, I was checked out by the general surgeon, who referred me to a specialist for the hysterectomy later on. My calendars filled up faster than my new breasts.

At this point, I felt like my own case manager. Dr. B hadn't been involved with the surgical activities, and now I was dealing with three different surgeons who specialized in three different areas of competence. I arranged the appointments, I told each what the other had said, and I wrote everything down. Of course, I couldn't drive yet, and Mike continued to take me to all appointments.

As for the Houston house, we postponed putting it on the market. I still needed to recuperate—still couldn't raise my arms very much. There was no way I could keep the house clean and vacate for potential buyers at the last minute. So, we decided to wait another month before officially listing it on the Multiple Listing System.

CHAPTER TWENTY FIVE

TOO PAINFUL TO REMEMBER

Date: 2/10/11
Subject: Merrily, we roll along

Hi all,
I'm over two weeks post-op and discovered I like having a retired husband. Although he's been great, I'm getting back to myself more every day. Tomorrow, I will shower and wash my own hair—and consider it an accomplishment.

Today I saw the oncologist. Although, in the end, the tumor wound up to be only one centimeter—right on the borderline for chemo—we're going ahead with the chemo. Considering my history, particularly with the BRCA1 gene, I concur—as much as I hate to admit it. So starting this Tuesday, I'm back on a schedule for six infusions, three weeks apart. May 31st should be the last one, but who's counting?

Tomorrow I'm playing Mahjong and trying to get my life back on track. We'll go to Florida next week as planned because of the new house—we need to pick options. (First I need to develop taste.) Fortunately, there's a decorator who'll help.

The writing is coming again, but slowly. Someone once pointed out that if you write one page a day, by the end of the year, you'd have a complete book. I'm doing about two pages and finding a rhythm to that. So, it's not too bad.

There are more surgeries at the other end of the chemo period, but I can't worry about that now. I'm in the one-day-at-a-time mode.

Oh, yeah, want to know about the girls? Little speed bumps. I haven't looked like this since I was nine. But things change rapidly in the land of plastic surgery. On Monday, I'll be fifteen.

Love, Linda

#

My chemo began on Tuesday, February 15th, exactly three weeks after my surgery. As soon as Mike and I walked into Dr. B's clinic, we heard a bell ringing. Hard. Loud. And long. I turned to Grace.

"What's going on?"

"Today's her last round of chemo so we celebrate. She's doing a good job shaking that bell, isn't she?"

Well, sure, judging by the crowd that gathered round, by the applause they bestowed and by the smile on the patient's face.

"Good for her," I said, my voice sharp, jealousy rearing its ugly head. That woman was done with her rounds of chemo and nausea and all the crap that went with it, while I was just starting. I forced myself to relax and turned to my own affairs.

This time the chemical cocktail would combine Taxotere with Cytoxan.

When I met with Dr. B, he handed me a printed sheet of side effects associated with each of them. Of course, hair loss appeared on both. But then there were other matters, such as peeling skin, hypersensitivity, fever, chills, joint pain, low blood counts, mouth sores, weakness, tiredness, tingling of hands and feet, fluid retention, mild nausea and vomiting and metallic taste.

"Patients react differently, and this doesn't mean you'll have any or all of these side effects. Some people have very mild cases. So, don't worry about it yet."

The list could have overwhelmed me, but I all I did was tuck the papers into my purse. I just didn't want to know everything right then. Instead, I hopped onto my comfortable lounge chair and let the treatment begin.

Grace accessed my new portacath, and within fifteen minutes, I became sleepy thanks to an initial infusion of Benadryl. A lovely feeling. I lay underneath a couple of warm blankets and felt awfully good for someone receiving the dreaded chemo. The time drifted. Mike and I chatted, I dozed, and then we were walking back to the car. The first session was over.

The next day, I returned for the Neulasta shot, which stimulates white blood cells needed to fight infection. I also remembered to take the two little steroid pills for the two required days. So, a new routine was developing, one I'd follow for six cycles instead of four.

In the meantime, Florida waited. One visit would do to pick our options for the house so the builder could begin construction. The right time was now, immediately after the first chemo, before I lost my hair again, and before the chemicals in my body became concentrated and other side effects apparent. We decided to drive the thousand miles not only to avoid crowds, but also so we'd have a car at hand when we arrived.

I worried about my oldest granddaughter. At seven, she was smart and observant. I couldn't lift her, cuddle her too closely or run around and play. Without reconstruction, the surgical recovery would have been faster and easier. But I wanted to look like my normal self later on, so I hopped on the local choo-choo instead of the express train to recovery.

"Grandma, where was your operation?"

"In my body."

"But where in your body?"

"In my chest."

"Oh."

And that, my friends, is the complete transcript of the "big" conversation between Granddaughter #1 and me. The KISS method won again. If ever I needed comic relief, now was the time, and my little sweetheart had provided it. I'll remember this conversation forever.

We tend to forget pain. As the old story goes, if we remembered the pain of childbirth, there'd be a lot more only children running around. In addition to giving birth three times, I'd had other surgeries in my life, one of which took several weeks to recover from. But none of my experiences had prepared me for the truth I noted on my laptop during the ride back from Florida, a truth I did not share with my friends in my emails to them:

Pain—the thing about pain after an operation like mine, and by that I mean an amputation, is that the discomfort is unrelenting. Whether I sit, eat a sandwich, or take a walk, the pain is with me. It is as loyal as a shadow, a constant companion.

Four weeks and two days have passed since the surgery, and I am still hurting. My skin is sensitive to touch; my foobs feel like rocks—tight and heavy—as if canned vegetables are hanging from my chest.

Funny isn't working anymore. It used to work in the beginning, but now it's hard to make jokes. I'm riding in the car, and I can't stand the pressure/pain of the seatbelt against me. I've placed a hank of yarn between the belt and my shoulder, but it doesn't help. My skin is too sensitive from the scraping inside and excision of breast tissue. I can feel everything. It's the tactile equivalent of chalk squealing against a blackboard.

This is what helps: a hydrocodone pill followed by a piece of chocolate. The perfect combination.

Crying helps. Every two days, I cry for about thirty seconds, and I feel better.

I can enumerate all I've been through during the last four weeks, but there's only one bottom line: I am a carrier of the BRCA1 gene mutation. Anger, disgust, sorrow—most of all, sorrow—at foisting this upon my family. Because my immediate family will need to be tested, too. So much to absorb and accept. Too much! This is happening to me. My nifty body has betrayed me.

I wonder if I'll ever be in good shape again. After years of exercise, choosing healthy foods (mostly), of taking pride in keeping a trim figure and healthy body...for what? I watch others jog by, or carry a baby and wonder if I'll ever be strong enough to lift weight again. Or walk a treadmill.

Food tastes off now. Isn't it too early for that? After two hours of choosing options for the new house a couple of days ago, I needed a break. I was exhausted. But lunch tasted good that day, and I felt better mentally, too.

Coping with breast cancer will be never-ending. It will be part of me for the rest of my life, for however long that is. I'm actually betting on a normal life span. The lymph nodes were clean. Clean! I elected to take chemo to attack any cancer cell that may have gotten away somehow, perhaps through the blood stream. I've decided to stick with the docs in Houston even after we move to Florida. An annual trip back is worth it.

This recuperation is harder than any other I've known. I'm acutely dependent on others and will continue to be for a long time, which makes me sad. My knight has been, and continues to be, the most wonderful support a gal can have. I'm a lucky woman.

CHAPTER TWENTY SIX

IN THE LOOP...ALWAYS IN THE LOOP

Date: 3/6/11
Subject: No Bad Hair Days

Hi everyone: It's been a little while, so here's a bit of catching up—

The hair update: Her name is Sky and she's my new best friend—for now. She's so loaded with attitude; however, I might be tempted to keep her around longer than planned. I now understand Tina Turner and Dolly Parton and why hanging onto Sky's cousins is their way of life. My headgear is gorgeous. The color's great—how could any color called "mochaccino" be anything but great with all the blond and blended highlights? The style is cute, sassy and so unlike my own style that I keep looking in the mirror. Who is that woman?

Sky was the very last wig I'd tried on. By that time,

I was worried about leaving the boutique with nothing. The catalogs pictured many possibilities, but they had to be ordered. Who had time for that? So, I kept opening the boxes on hand and eventually found Sky. A great choice, but very different than Betty.

My own hair falls out in fits and starts, in tufts and strands. It doesn't all lay on a pillow one morning in a huge mess. So, there's a built-in anxiety once the disappearing act starts as to when it will end. To alleviate that anxiety, we shaved my head. SO THERE. I'm in charge now. I'm not waiting around for the inevitable. Can you tell I've got to claim control over something? So, for the second time in my life, I sat on the back patio and handed the clippers to Mike. Ten years ago, I cried. This time, I just said to get on with it.

The boob update: Around my house, we call them Frankenfoobs. They're ugly lumps and they hurt a lot. It feels as if I'm carrying around two fifty-pound rocks. Right now, there are expanders inside my chest behind my pectoral muscles, which is part of the implant preparedness process. It's a good thing I started this when I had the original surgery, because I would never have gone back to get implants after healing flat. Who knew how painful this would be? Dr. B, my oncologist, joked that surgeons always underestimate the pain of recovery and oncologists always underestimate the discomfort of chemo. Except he didn't. He's been fantastic.

So, I keep thinking about those perky rewards I'll get sometime...maybe six months? But six months seems like forever right now. Fortunately, I've got plenty to keep me busy besides medical appointments. We're putting the house on the market this week (Realtor coming on Monday); writing a book or two (which is not happening, but I keep thinking about it), and posting emails to my friends.

I hope all is well with everyone and that your heart's desire is always within reach.
Love, Linda

#

The boxes on the March 2011 calendar were almost full. If I wasn't going for a chemo treatment—two that month—plus the day-after Neulasta shot, I was going for an expander fill at the plastic surgeon's office. Or home buyers were scheduled for a look-see at the house. Which meant I had to find somewhere else to go for two hours.

I looked forward to Wednesday lunches during this period. The three-week chemo schedule structured my life in general, but I could visit with friends during the periods I felt well. My dear friend, Pat Rosen, usually showed up with delicious tuna or chicken salad sandwiches, but more importantly, made time in her busy day to share an hour or two with me. I loved the company, and we had a lot to talk about, with writing and our current projects heading the list. Sometimes our third critique partner, Pat Kay, joined us, and the conversation ran non-stop.

These visits reminded me of my non-cancer, happier life full of imaginary heroines and heroes, conflicts and troubles which were resolved by the end of the story. Why do we write romance novels? This is a question that is discussed by writers time and again. The answer? Romance is the one genre where we can guarantee the happily-ever-after readers and writers both yearn for. Although our real lives may be less than perfect, we can make sure our flawed heroes and heroines wind up in the arms of their perfect match.

Writing-wise, however, I was now exploring the realm of Women's Fiction, where the focus of the story is on the woman's journey through a crisis or a challenge. Romantic elements can play a part, but the love story is secondary. These stories—usually dramatic—are more complex in their themes and contain substantial subplots. The main story line shows the protagonist coping with such things as a divorce, death, an ill child or an unexpected opportunity that takes her miles from her comfortable world. (Look up anything by Elizabeth Berg, Jodi Picoult, Barbara O'Neal, Bridget Asher or Barbara Delinsky.) I seem to focus on stories involving families in crisis. I had no idea, however, if either project I was working on would ever rest in a reader's hands.

Having a creative writing challenge helped distract me from my discomfort. I never asked for pain medication after the initial surgery, not because I'm a martyr, but because I just didn't think to ask. So, the only pain-free time I had was when I sat still and didn't move my arms.

Time. I simply needed more time to heal. That's what I told myself and hoped it was true. Meanwhile, I kept my fingers on the keyboard.

#

Date: 4/06/2011
Subject: And the Beat Goes On

Ready for your monthly Linda update?
We're starting with great news. My sister is NOT a gene carrier for this crappy disease. Just found out yesterday, and I had to spread the word. This also means that my niece is in the clear, too. Justice must triumph sometimes. Of course, my boys seem to be taking their own sweet time about their tests, but I don't want to nag...at least, not yet.

The extra special treat is that Judy (sister) is flying in today and will be with me until Monday. I can't express how happy I am about the visit. She is, too. And as a true New Yorker, she's bringing a dozen bialys with her. She knows what makes me happy. I'm figuring this sophisticated bunch all know what bialys are. (But just in case, they're similar to, but chewier than, bagels and have an onion flavor and onion bits on them; simply delicious).

I'm halfway through the chemo. Three down and three to go. Since it's now April, I can say that I'll be done next month—even if the very last treatment is on the very last day of May. But who's counting? The side effects have been relatively mild, and each month is a little different from the last. This month, my fingernails hurt. Is this ridiculous or what? But they do. No nausea, no fevers—so I'll take fingernails.

The foobs are another matter. They shift, they hurt, they're hard and feel like rocks on my chest. I swear that after all this, and after the exchange is made from expanders to the real implants, I'd better wind up with the prettiest set in Florida. I think doctors are all in cahoots. No one mentioned how uncomfortable this in-between time would be. So, maybe ignorance is bliss. Maybe I wouldn't have had the cojones to go through with it. OTOH—I "enjoy being a girl"—so maybe I would have. Moot now.

Other stuff—Do you hear the pounding of my head against the brick wall? That's the sound of me trying to sell this house. Every house hunter watches too much HGTV! They all want perfection. Which means they want to buy, move in, and start living. No work. No changes. Everything has to be move-in ready. We've already invested over $10K to be "move-in ready." Removed the wallpaper and painted instead, removed drapes, bought new appliances (stainless steel only), *installed new backsplash in kitchen. I should have done all this a few years ago and enjoyed using the stuff myself. But really, there was nothing wrong with my double ovens! Except for the color: white. I can picture my Depression-era parents rolling in their graves. So wasteful!*

Sending hugs and cyber bubbly to all. Please keep in touch. I want to know what's happening as I stay close to my nest.

Love, Linda

#

Judy was with us for my three-month check-up with the general surgeon and my first meeting with the ob-gyn surgeon. This specialist would perform the oophorectomy right after Dr. R inserted the breast implants. Seemed I always needed two docs in the OR at the same time. Others had told me that the removal of my ovaries and fallopian tubes would be done using laparoscopic technique, but it was a relief to hear it from the surgeon who would actually be hands-on.

I'd never lacked confidence in my doctors, starting with Dr. B, and that confidence continued with this ob-gyn surgeon, who'd been highly recommend by my general surgeon—recommended for a good reason. My general surgeon had been operated on by the same doctor! You can't get a higher endorsement than that. I knew the ob-gyn specialist would be as excellent as my other physicians, but as I said to my sister, "By the time they're done with me, I'll be a neutered cat!"

#

I've often mentioned here how the frankenfoobs were killing me. The discomfort—a-hem, pain—was constant and time's passing didn't seem to be easing it. So, I made a decision to postpone my fills. Whether I was a wimp or perhaps more sensitive to the pain than most other patients, I don't know. But I couldn't continue with both the chemo and the fill injections simultaneously. Dr. R wasn't too happy. My knight had reservations. Mike was concerned that a postponement would delay the end date of the fill procedure and postpone the date of the final exchange surgery, when the real implants would be inserted.

The men, however, weren't living in my body. They weren't feeling what I felt every minute of every day and night. They weren't dealing with the chemo's side effects—my toes were so discolored and sensitive I couldn't bear the weight of a top sheet let alone a sock or shoe—so I made the call to postpone.

I took a five-week break from the fills and just dealt with the chemo and selling the house. That decision turned out to be a big mistake that I paid for later, after the move to Florida.

CHAPTER TWENTY SEVEN

THAT'S WHAT FRIENDS ARE FOR

On the evening of my fourth chemo, Mike and I joined a group of friends to celebrate Passover. When we were first invited, I hesitated accepting, unsure how I'd be feeling that night. In the end, however, I was very glad to be at Anne and Marty's house, chatting with others, joining in the Seder dinner, helping to retell the Exodus story and thinking about anything other than cancer. On the way home, I laughed at myself for once more proving that when you focus on others, you worry less about yourself. A wonderful way to live. I vowed to remember that no matter how crappy I felt.

Three weeks later, I had my fifth chemo and sent out this email shortly afterwards:

Date: 5/15/11
Subject: "Just keep swimming." - Dory, from Finding Nemo

I'm with Dory, swimming, swimming and finally

heading toward the shore. Five chemos down and only one to go. May 31st will be it. Then a three week recovery period of which only a few days are yucky. Not too bad now that the end is really in sight ☺ (Wine has helped.)

Selling the house remains an on-going challenge especially in the "getting ready to show" part. A few days ago, we had ninety minutes to prepare for a showing. Today we had three hours. Of course, I've been keeping the house clean in general, but…geez, we have to put our garbage pail and newspapers in the garage, sweep floors, turn on all lights and fans upstairs and down…a regular drill. All I know is that we might wind up owning two houses. Not in the plan, but hey, we're flexible. Right? I might be a landlord before this is all done. But Florida awaits. And we are going.

The foobs are still a royal pain. Literally. If I don't wind up loving them after the exchange surgery, I'll be very disappointed. I will yell, scream and cry, and that will not be a nice scenario at all.

I know I've mentioned Ninc before, but the October writers' conference has become a goal for me. I'm looking forward to seeing those of you who are going.

Stay well everyone, and celebrate your happy times with gusto.

Love, Linda

#

On May 31st, two weeks after I sent that email, I sat on Dr. Bernicker's recliner, dozing on Benadryl for the last time. Chemo number six. Mike was with me, as always, making sure the IV pole didn't fall over as I made my way to the restroom every hour or so. When a lot of liquid goes in, it soon wants to come out.

Dr. B had been in to see me; the nurses had set me

up and chatted. The chemo routine itself had become familiar and surprisingly comfortable. I'd known the staff for ten years. They'd become my cheering squad. Sooner or later, however, even the most adored routine ends, and this one—less adored than suffered through—was about to end. Not soon enough for me, or my painful fingers, toes and swollen ankles. I was tired of being tired. Tired of being bald. Tired of having cancer! But damn glad to be alive.

I watched the IV bags being replaced, one after the other. First one drug, then the other, and then the saline. I watched drop after drop as the liquid flowed slowly down the lines; I watched the plastic bags collapse upon themselves as the drugs disappeared into my portacath. I watched until there were no more bags, no more liquid. I watched Grace come into the room and detach me from the IV.

My gaze went from Mike to her. "It's over," I said. "Number six is done."

Mike's hand tightened on mine. Grace nodded, told me to get dressed and go outside to the admin desk. I felt a smile start to emerge. I was more than ready to be checked out.

A small crowd awaited me in the hall. Grace held out a bell. "Ring it," she ordered. "It's your turn now."

I'd forgotten all about this intimate celebration of accomplishment. Forgotten about the clanging bell I'd heard on the day of my very first chemo appointment almost six months ago. And now I reached for the bell. Shook it, but dang, it hardly made a sound for me. Grace reached over. "Come on. Let's do it right." With her help—again I needed her help—we rang that bell so it could be heard throughout the entire clinic. Then came the applause. And my tears.

I enjoyed the moment, knowing it was but a moment, one station along an ever-winding road. Ahead of me loomed more visits to the plastic surgeon in order to continue the fills I'd put on hold. Ahead also loomed two more big surgeries. But at that moment, my final chemo deserved some acknowledgement, so we took a moment to bask in the afterglow of coming through it. And I sent a silent apology to the woman I'd seen doing the same thing at my first visit.

When we got home, I called the plastic surgeon's office and made an appointment for another fill two weeks later. I wanted to metabolize the last chemo first. Waiting was a mistake. We needed a three-month wait between the final fill and the exchange surgery when Dr. R would remove the expanders and insert the real implants, which put that surgery at the end of September. I'd gotten confused thinking the three-month wait was from the time of the last chemo on May 31st, which would have put the surgery at the end of August. That difference between the final chemo and the final fill would usually not be a big deal. Unless you're moving out of state and something goes wrong.

\#

A Publishing Revolution Arrives

Ten years ago, Murphy's law covered my new job, breast cancer and my debut novel—the beginning of a second career. Now Murphy incorporated an out-of-state move, more breast cancer and a publishing revolution that affected every author on the planet. You might wonder why attending a writers' conference was so important when I didn't have a new book to unveil. The answer is that a writer's career is a long-distance marathon, usually on a road scattered with potholes and boulders as well as smooth blacktop. Good reviews and good sales numbers define happiness. But dry spells or life "getting in the way" defines worry.

The ups and downs, however, reminded me of the ups and downs in other areas of life such as marriage, child rearing and friendships. When you're in for the long haul, constant effort is required; highs and lows are expected. I'd kept writing through the chemos because that's what I like to do. The words came slowly as I worked on *Family Interrupted*, the story of a family in crisis told from each person's point-of-view. My turtle's pace toward the finish line didn't bother me. The fact that I could concentrate and weave together a more complex story than I'd ever written in the past absolutely thrilled me. Chemo be damned! Pain be damned. Writers write. That's the truth and not complex at all.

I wanted to attend conferences and catch up with industry news even if I went to bed early. I had to spend some money, but I considered it a definite investment in my stalled career. That year, 2011, Novelists, Inc. would once again gather at a hotel on St. Pete's beach. I'd be living in Florida by then, and the venue was perfect for me, less than an hour's drive.

As I mentioned earlier, the conversations at the last year's meeting were filled with shouts and whispers about authors taking more control of their work and publishing their books independently. Online. The advent of electronic readers kick-started the movement, while the success of a few daring authors reinforced the idea. It was the powerhouse, Amazon, quickly followed by Barnes & Noble and others, that created an environment for indie publishing that was hard to ignore.

Authors now had the freedom—along with new responsibilities—to publish their own books. They would set the price. Determine the length. Choose the release date. Provide print editions, if they so desired. Publish more books in a timely manner. And earn more money in royalties than a traditional publisher could offer. The times, they were a-changing.

Of course, nothing worthwhile is easy. The responsibilities for story editing, copyediting, cover design and pushing hard to promote the book fell totally on the author. Facebook, anyone? How about Twitter? Those social networks were now seen as something more than merely keeping up with friends and family. They became the gateway to "getting the word out" about the books. The word on everyone's tongue was "discoverability."

The idea of self-publishing excited me, but frightened me, too. I loved the idea of having control over my career, writing the stories I wanted to write at my own pace. I'm a writer, and writers write. They like to write. They want to write. Publishers don't write. Their job is to get the books out. In the new paradigm, I'd be my own publisher. I might have less time for creating stories.

Like a siren song, however, the thought of being my own boss tantalized, always teasing in the back of my mind. I wouldn't need an agent, wouldn't have to give up fifteen percent of whatever I earned. Of course, if no one bought the book, I wouldn't earn anything at all! Promotion could eat my life.

So, true to form, I put my head in the sand and procrastinated making that decision. Instead, I kept working on stories, sticking to the task I most enjoyed. I knew, however, I'd learn the latest industry news at the next conference in October. My frankenfoobs would be gone by then, replaced by a pair of beauties, which wouldn't hurt or would hurt less. I'd settle for that.

On June 21st, I received my last fill. The exchange surgery as well as the oophorectomy were scheduled for September 21st. I'd barely have two weeks to recover before leaving Houston at the beginning of October as planned. Part of me was scared. Part of me excited. I wanted to start the next stage of my life, but wanted to be healthy while doing it.

My last appointment with Dr. Bernicker had me close to tears. A real approach/avoidance event. I hated to leave him. My security blanket. My trusted physician. My friend. Dr. B explained why I'd be taking a hormone inhibitor for the next five years. One pill daily would reduce the amount of estrogen my body made, a necessary decision because my second cancer was measured at a 15% estrogen level. I took my first pill on July 1st and made a mental note of the date. As I write this, I'm approaching the two-year mark. Still a long way to go.

Side effects? Yes. Thin hair, some joint pain and fatigue. All bearable for me. For others, it's much worse. Current research may lengthen the treatment to ten years. I intend to be around to finish the course!

CHAPTER TWENTY EIGHT

HI-HO, HI-HO, TO FLORIDA WE GO

Despite our best efforts, selling the house proved impossible, so we decided to lease it. A stroke of good luck coupled with good real estate agents brought our current tenants to us, and we signed a lease to start October 5th. That lease made the move real. We were leaving Houston, our home for the past sixteen years.

The summer passed in a flurry of chores, packing, donating, cleaning—always cleaning—and throwing out! Amazing what can accumulate in closets, drawers and nooks, and on shelves in the house and garage. I love big bags with handles. Easier to bring stuff to Goodwill, the stuff that's too good to throw away, but not wanted anymore.

September came. So did the surgeries. Here is the last group email I sent to my friends:

Date: 9/24/2011
Subject: The Fat Lady Has Sung…and that's a good thing!

Hi everyone!

It's over, it's over, it's over. The final surgeries are done. I'm relieved and thrilled to be looking at this challenging year in the rearview mirror.

The two surgeries were performed on Wednesday. I am now a neutered cat, but hopefully with a few lives still ahead of me. Laparoscopic surgery is great, except for the carbon dioxide pumped into you, giving the doc room to work in order to remove the ovaries. Unfortunately, the CO2 takes forever to escape later and often burns your shoulders. Isn't that weird? But true. Who knew?

Now let's talk foobs. I was disappointed at first—don't know what I was thinking or drinking—because what I saw wasn't the me I knew. I wanted to look in the mirror and see my old self (minus the nips and areolas) but still recognize that, yes, it was me. Well, it wasn't and isn't and couldn't be.

The radiation I'd had ten years ago prevented the skin on one side from expanding enough to accommodate the size I'd been. So, after a few minutes of disappointment, I decided the gals in the mirror seemed nice enough, and we'd get along just fine. They looked very, very good under camisoles. I tried on five!

My friends in Houston have filled my fridge with such wonderful comfort foods that I'm recovering quickly. I feel like a fraud eating everything. We've leased our house for the next year, and on October 5th, we'll start the trek to our new home in Florida. We look forward to many gatherings of family (yay, grandkids) and friends.

Here's to the Ninc conference, books, stories and new manuscripts. Life is sweet. Enjoy!

Love to all, Linda

Suddenly, we were off. I trailed Mike in our old car,

which was second nature for me to handle, as we drove the thousand miles. We covered four hundred miles a day. Normally, we make the trip in one big session—about a sixteen-hour drive with a couple of quick stops. That wasn't going to happen this time. My boobs still made themselves known for their discomfort. A little less than before, but I couldn't forget about them. Sky still covered my head. I yearned for the time when her services would no longer be needed. On the outside, I was heading toward Florida. On the inside, I was heading toward normal. Please, God, no more challenges!

#

Writers in Charge… Are You Talking about Me?

For me, a house becomes a home when the pictures are hung and visitors show up. Within two weeks, I was comfortable in our new digs. I met a few neighbors; our son helped Mike hang light fixtures while I fed the family crew, which included my biggest grandgirl. I joined a book club, started exercising in the fitness center, and of course, set up my writing office in a guest bedroom. With my computer up and running, I was happy to get back to work. On the fiction side, I eventually chose to work exclusively on *Family Interrupted,* which turned out to be my very first self-published novel. It "went live" in April 2013. On the non-fiction side, this memoir kept me constant company. As important as the writing was, however, it couldn't compete with the thrill of living close to family for the first time since our sons reached adulthood and established their own lives. Now, Grandpa and I resided close to grandchildren. Mission accomplished!

After the pictures graced our walls, Mike and I

packed a bag, and for the second time, headed to St. Pete's Beach for the Novelist, Inc. conference. I was happy to have him along. Frankly, I didn't want to share a room with another author at this time. Between the fatigue, wig, and my groaning as I moved around, rooming with me would have been a punishment no one deserved. So, my tinfoil knight was at my side, delighted to attend. What's not to like at a beach resort?

Once more, I realized how much the publishing industry was evolving. The title of this conference, *New Rules! New Tools! WRITERS IN CHARGE*, said it all. Authors had a lot to learn and evaluate. We had decisions to make, career-altering decisions. The evolution seemed like a revolution—quick changes in process, power and remuneration. A new freedom, which frightened as much as it attracted, similar in my mind to the lure of democracy for those who've never experienced it.

Into this whirlwind of new information, Mike and I ventured with curiosity and interest. Yes, Mike, too. Despite the distractions of a beautiful beach and fishing rods, my hubby had to earn his keep. His work assignment included accompanying me to the first day's panel discussions—and remembering everything! Books are my business, but Mike has always been involved whether critiquing a male character's dialog in a story (Would a guy really say that?), helping select a new computer or cheering me on with my career. During the panel discussions, I'd take notes on my little AlphaSmart while Mike's phenomenal memory and reasoning skills would be well engaged.

The idea of writing this memoir had been percolating in the back of my mind for a while. One of the authors at the conference was also a photographer, and I had her take my picture twice: once while wearing my sassy wig, and once while not. I wanted the pictures for the record—to use only with the memoir, if I decided to go forward. Knowing how I like to imagine happy endings and leave the garbage behind, I would never have had the shots taken if it weren't for this book's possibility. My family didn't need a visual remembrance. As for me, could I ever forget?

To say I received the warmest of welcomes at the conference would be an understatement. From close friends who'd received my periodic email reports to new friends who wished me well, I felt surrounded by Ninc's caring community of writers and their spouses. Other women there knew exactly what I'd gone through because, let's face it, if one out of eight gets the disease, chances were good that several survivors attended that meeting. In fact, that hypothetical turned out to be true.

I worked hard each day—workshops, panels, seminars, socializing, typing away on the AlphaSmart and filling its files with notes—but never made it to one evening activity. In 2011, I was not a night owl. Instead, Mike and I wended our way back to our room after dinner where I got undressed as soon as possible and crawled under the sheets. My chest still hurt, and the hurting disconcerted me. I constantly reminded myself that only a month had passed since the exchange surgery. The girls looked fine, so I tried to toughen up and groan quietly.

The palpable air of excitement seeped into my writer's soul at the conference. By the end of the weekend, most authors who'd decided to publish their own books spoke about gathering together again the following year and comparing notes on how far they'd gotten in their efforts. I, too, had decided to go the indie route. The Do-It-Yourself era had arrived, and we were all on information overload—so much to learn about the process of producing books electronically, but hopefully worth the effort. My writing mission was clear: Finish

Family Interrupted and jump into the deep end of the new publishing world.

CHAPTER TWENTY NINE

THE HUNT FOR DR. WONDERFUL

Tampa Bay Area, FL
October 2011

We had another mission: Find top-level doctors in Florida. If you've ever experienced a major relocation, you understand the challenge. Finding just any physician is not difficult. Finding a physician you trust? Not so easy. My strategy was to search for an internist first, and with that doctor, discuss referrals for oncology specialists. Although I intended to visit Dr. Bernicker again, I knew I needed local boots on the ground as well. Moffitt Cancer Center, a very reputable institution in Tampa, seemed like a good fit, and after doing some online research, I came up with the name of a medical oncologist who looked promising. I showed Dr. Bernicker her resume, and he agreed that Dr. Minton was the type of doctor I needed.

But first, I needed an internist. After making inquiries among my new neighbors, one doctor came highly recommended. I quickly made an appointment, hoping to establish a good rapport and update some prescription refills. To my great relief, Dr. T came across as smart and professional. She asked direct questions, digging out my history and took my cancer experience and implants in stride. I liked her and felt comfortable. My only criticism concerned the administrative side of the office. The staff still used old-fashioned manila file folders; the lack of computerization surprised me.

Dr. T had some knowledge of the oncologist I'd discovered and, considering Dr. Bernicker liked her on paper, I'd try this oncologist first. I called the Moffitt Center for an appointment with Dr. Minton, the head of the Breast Oncology department. It should have been a simple task. Make a phone call, book an appointment. But it was not simple. Prior to scheduling me in, I had to procure the documentation for my entire breast cancer history. Twelve years worth of documentation. That's right. Twelve years. Medical records from every surgeon who'd ever touched me. That included my initial lumpectomy, lab reports, radiation reports, glass slides— would you believe, glass slides? The brutal record gathering required the administrative skills of an Executive Secretary, and suddenly, I found myself in that role.

I created charts for each hospital or clinic that had treated me. I kept hand written records of my conversations—the contacts, directives and dates. I kept records of what I sent in to Moffitt and to which of two addresses they were sent. I printed copies of every letter and form I completed and returned to them. All this in order to get an appointment! To be fair, if I had just been diagnosed with the disease and needed active treatment, they would have scheduled me right in. But in my position as an unknown follow-up type of patient, I had to jump through hoops.

A month later, while I worked on the Moffitt project, I developed symptoms of infection. My right breast was hot to the touch, swollen and I ran a temperature of almost 103 degrees. I didn't panic immediately because I had a doctor to call now, my new internist. Dr. T put me on strong antibiotics, but after two days nothing changed. My situation challenged her skills and her license.

She then supplied the names of three breast oncology surgeons. A new quest had begun. None of the three could see me, and I felt the first stirrings of panic seeping in. Each office suggested someone else. The phone was now an extension of my ear as my stress escalated. I followed every single lead until finally at three o'clock on a Thursday afternoon, seven weeks after moving to The Sunshine State, I spoke with the appointment desk at the University of South Florida, across the street from Tampa General Hospital.

"Her schedule is full," the secretary said, referring the breast surgeon. "She was at Moffitt this morning, and now she's here, and she's so busy, but—but you sound like such a nice lady."

"I am a nice lady!" I replied, sensing a heart in this woman. "And I really need help."

"Uh…okay. If you can get here at five o'clock—"

"I'll be there. No problem. Thank you so much." And thank God for the GPS we'd bought! Mike and I arrived at the registration desk at 4:45 that afternoon. I filled out a mess of papers, signed them and at 5:30, met my new surgeon, whom everyone referred to as Dr. D because of her hard-to-pronounce last name.

I will never forget our exchange. After examining me, Dr. D said, "If you were my patient, you'd be in the

OR tomorrow morning."

Looking her straight in the eye, I said, "I am now your patient. So what are we waiting for?"

And with that, she made the arrangements, and I walked across the street, checked myself into Tampa General wearing only the clothes on my back, and braced myself for another surgery. It was December 1st. I'd been in Florida less than two months and had no choice but to face another unexpected situation. Sometimes, events happen at a fast pace. I thought about my sons and daughters-in-law, my sister, my friends back in Houston. Except for my son, Andy, a respiratory therapist at the hospital, none of them would know anything about what happened until after the operation was over. But perhaps it's better that way. My dear ones would have less time to wonder and worry. I knew Andy would stick his head in my door the next day, then spread the word to his brothers.

Trying to prepare for whatever happened next, I gave Dr. D the technical implant information—manufacturer, size, serial number—so she could replace it with a new one after cleaning out the infection and putting me on IV drips. Anyway, that was the plan. In essence, I'd be starting over, starting clean.

Were there other surgeries I could have considered? Yes. All in the Flap Family: TRAM, DIEP, Gluteal, and LAT. Currently, there's another one called TUG. Each one of these reconstructive surgeries required many hours on the operating table—as many as sixteen—and are appropriate only for specific groups of patients. For example, I didn't have enough belly fat to consider a TRAM Flap, the one that provides a "tummy tuck" bonus to patients. So, I put my hopes on another implant, but knew there were no guarantees.

In the OR the next morning, everything moved like clockwork. The staff was great, friendly, professional and on time! At this point, medical procedures didn't frighten me very much. But just like any patient, I wanted it over and done with, and with a good outcome.

Funny how priorities can change. With a clean bill of cancer health, I now focused on my boobs. I wanted two that matched. Should I have given thanks only for my good health and not cared about my appearance? Should I have been content simply to be alive? I discovered that priorities shift after you surmount that ultimate goal of survival. Suddenly, I felt like the ubiquitous "every woman" who wanted to look as good as she could look. I was alive. In-your-face alive. My own concept of femininity mattered, and I reached once more for "normal." Normal for Linda, that is.

#

"You can't always get what you wa-a-nt,"
Rolling Stones

I woke up flat on one side. Dr. D could not replace the implant due to the amount of fluid buildup, poor, thin-quality skin and no AlloDerm—a mesh that had to be removed—to hold the implant. Other than all that, I was a great candidate for another implant! Nope, not gonna happen.

From that little place way down deep inside where truth resides, I'd suspected this outcome. I was disappointed, but not totally surprised. That little place of truth also revealed something else, too. *I'd had enough.* Enough worry, enough pain, enough surgery. Especially surgery. From now on, my matched set would have to be compliments of a prosthetic breast inserted into a special bra manufactured for that purpose.

Regardless of my decision, I needed time to adjust to it. Until this moment, through all the procedures in

Houston, I'd had two breasts. So what if they weren't natural. So what if they were make-believe. I'd had two of them, and they'd looked good. Through it all, my body looked similar to what I'd seen in the mirror every day of my adult life.

The phone calls from my sons the next afternoon began with, "You're not doing anything else, are you?" and "You're done, right?" and from my daughter-in-law, "We don't care. We love you. You don't need any more surgeries." Of course, I teared up, but despite my own decision, I held off on a one hundred percent promise. In my world, promises are real; promises are kept. I wasn't quite ready to commit. Never make decisions in the heat of a moment. Or when you're in temporary pain.

"I'm probably done with surgeries," I said. "I'm ninety-eight percent sure."

After five days in the hospital being cared for by the kind of nurses who keep you company in the middle of the night, the kind of nurses for whom I wrote letters of appreciation—I went home with a PICC line in my arm. The PICC line allowed me to self-administer antibiotics via an IV hookup for ten days. Naturally, Mike helped me handle the apparatus. It was more clumsy than difficult, and we lucked out in that the timing was great. The eleventh day brought our youngest son and his family to visit for the holiday week.

Florida is definitely a magnet to Northerners during the winter months, but I had a feeling that Grandma Linda and Papa Mike were magnets, too. Holding those grandbabies lifted my spirits like nothing else could. Our middle son flew in from Tulsa, and for the first time in quite a while, the entire Barrett family was under one roof. My roof!

Although I took it fairly easy, I made sure not to be left out of any exciting activity. One visit I'll always remember was to the Jungle Gardens in Sarasota where my four-year-old grandgirl almost fell into the flamingo pond. I saw her step too close and slip. I yelled out. Mike sprinted forward and caught her. She then turned to her papa and, with the sincerity of a thankful child, exclaimed, "Papa, you saved me!"

Of course he had. A trusted knight always comes through.

That family gathering was the highlight of my year, eclipsing all medical issues, pain, surgeries and the thousand-mile move. Three sons, both daughters-in-law, four grandkids and Jessie the Schnoodle (a hypoallergenic combo of Schnauzer and Poodle)—all visiting Mike and me at the same time. We were noisy. Loud. Holding a million conversations at once. Lighting Hanukkah candles. Painting and coloring pictures and playing games. Blowing bubbles. The kitchen table was opened to double its usual size for the entire week. And naturally, the flamingo story was told over and over again, most often by my little sweetheart.

Family week. I couldn't get enough of it. I absorbed the scenes into my heart and soul. This is what I had fought for. This was the gift the doctors had given me. *Precious life.* I was luckier than some, and I knew it.

I hadn't gotten everything I wanted, but I did get exactly what I needed.

#

I Enjoy Being a Girl...With or Without My Tatas

In the weeks that followed, I visited my surgeon regularly for aftercare. The breast area kept filling with fluid, which had to be drained. Picture extraction by needle. Shopping for a bra was postponed until I fully healed.

I was stunned to learn the results of the pathology

tests. The lab found almost no bacteria in all that fluid. In the end, my body had rejected the implant not because of the product itself—implants are inert—but because of my own body's characteristics, such as possible poor skin quality due to the radiation ten years ago, poor drainage due to multiple surgeries and/or loss of lymph nodes or a mild infection, which escalates the rejection. Despite my excellent plastic surgeon in Houston who studied my history and examined me thoroughly, a combination of these may have caused my situation. Regardless of the details, I could not and would not consider another implant. I subsequently learned that fifteen percent of all implants resulted in this type failure.

Instead of another implant, I turned to Plan C. Using a prosthetic breast. I looked forward to visiting *Ladies First Choice*, a specialty shop for women like me who needed special bras with sleeves in which to slip the prosthesis. This niche clothing store offered a large variety of lingerie from bras to bathing suits as well as scarves and head wraps and beyond. More important, the staff of licensed fitters was not only skilled in measuring, but was friendly, patient and wise. They knew how to make me relax and feel at home with them.

I had fun! A dressing room is a dressing room. Trying on is trying on. How very familiar. In the end, I learned that shopping for a special bra is no different than shopping for any bra. I was just another woman concerned about support, fit and how I looked in clothes, especially sweaters, jerseys, or tee shirts. I tested every bra I considered by putting on a tee shirt and seeing how the material laid.

Applying eye makeup became a daily ritual instead of an occasional happening. I've continued to wear it every day. Psychologists would probably say that I'm compensating for my lost breast and asserting my femininity however I can. They'd be right. Am I reminding myself, or the world around me, of my womanhood? Let's face it—female breasts are special. Only a woman can nurse a child. Men ogle breasts because they don't have them. They are the essential part of the hourglass figure women strive for and men admire to the point of worship. In our youth-oriented, sex and glamour culture, it's hard to miss the importance put on breasts. Why else would so many women voluntarily enlarge them?

I had never been one of those women, but rather one of the group of "ordinary" women, millions of them, content with their gifts whether small or large. Now, I am simply a woman who was dealt a crummy genetic hand and learned to adjust her expectations.

I know that others have had a tougher journey on the cancer road than me. However, I can speak in detail only about my own journey which continues beyond today with semi-annual visits to my oncologist, daily ingestion of the hormone inhibitor and general alertness to body changes. "How do you feel?" is a question that makes me think before I reply.

More important to me, as a mom, is the uncertainty of my sons' statuses. They have chosen to postpone the knowing. I understand their decision. After all, I wore the Cleopatra robe at one time. But I worry about my family's future, both girls and boys. Males who carry the mutated gene have a higher breast cancer risk than men who don't carry the gene. So I worry, but I also hope. I hope that researchers will break the genetic code, identify in advance those who are marked for cancer, and be able to reverse that course. That is my hope. That is my prayer for us all.

CHAPTER THIRTY

DECISION TREES AND ALTERNATE UNIVERSES

Every decision, whether intentional or unintentional, brings with it its own set of future choices, particular outcomes, consequences and compromises. Life seems to work that way, and even more so when you're faced with life-threatening events. Perhaps I should have mapped out a decision tree way back at the time of the first diagnosis to see the possible consequences of all my choices. A decision tree is an excellent tool to help you choose between several courses of action. So, let's see...

If I had followed my first surgeon's advice and had a single mastectomy and no radiation, my reconstructive surgery probably would have been successful, and I would look and feel like a whole person. In some alternate universe, somewhere, there's another Linda Barrett walking around with a functioning left breast and a nice implant on the right. I kind of like that picture. But, let's take another look—

Removing my cancerous breast would have precluded a second bout of cancer in that breast, but would not have raised a red flag to have genetic testing. My ignorance of the BRCA1 gene might have resulted in more serious problems, such as ovarian cancer, later in life. Breast cancer is no picnic, but ovarian cancer has a much higher mortality rate. Ergo, I'm not so crazy about this picture.

What if I had continued to deny the lump I'd found in my breast? What if I finally saw Maya when the tumor had reached a Stage 3 or 4? How would my lymph nodes have been effected then?

On the plastic surgery side, what if I had proceeded with the expander fills on the doctor's schedule instead of stopping them for several weeks during my chemo? Had I made that decision, my complications would have occurred in Houston. I'd have raced to my doctor's office immediately, and the situation might have been resolved more successfully. Perhaps I would have been able to keep the implant.

Of course, if my son hadn't left Houston and relocated to Tulsa in the first place, I'd still have been in Texas instead of Florida.

So, do I take consolation in looking at a scarred chest minus the implant, realizing that I'm alive, healthy and enjoying family, friends and career? Or, do I waste time ruminating on how much better things *might* have turned out? That would mean, of course, that I ignore how much worse it could have been, too.

#

"And they lived happily ever after."
Linda Barrett, Romance writer

Tampa, Florida
Spring 2013

A year has passed since I began putting this story together. Once again, I'm sitting at the wrought iron table on the lanai, this time with a glass of wine in hand. In front of me are a spread of cheese and crackers, a bowl of hummus and a tray of veggies. Potato salad and cole slaw wait in the fridge along with a load of hotdogs and hamburgers. The kids are coming over soon. Perhaps we'll jump in the community pool or play some pickleball before lighting the grill. A sweet day with my family, at least the part that lives here. This dream has come true.

On the lawn, the sand hill cranes take their deliberate steps. They mate for life, and this year they've hatched five young ones who've grown quickly.

My medical folders are stored in a box on a closet shelf. They've served their purpose, and I don't need to reference them anymore. Hopefully, never again.

As for my knight, well, he's smiling at me, taking a break from his daily wrestle with the crossword puzzle.

"Happy?" he asks.

I stare at him as the sun shines through the screen, its light striking his face, illuminating the love he showers on me. "Very happy."

And so I am. Happy that *yesterday* has been examined and put to bed. Happy to be in this place and time. "We've finally arrived at the point you wanted to be last year," I say. "Our story continues in the here and now. One day at a time."

His smile becomes a grin. "Took you long enough to catch on."

I ignore his teasing. "We're making one little change though," I say, leaving my chair and walking toward him. I cup his face in my hands. "It's about the tinfoil," I explain between soft kisses. "It's all worn out."

He startles. "Are you kidding? It's barely been used. Not even a scratch."

He doesn't get it, and that is why I finally say, "You've been my Knight in Shining Tinfoil all these years, sweetheart, but the truth is—"

"Oh, hell, I'm being promoted?"

What the—? "*Fuhggedaboudit*! It'll take you another lifetime for this chance to come around again."

"That's just fine with me."

And I'm definitely on board.

The End

ACKNOWLEDGEMENTS

You don't ride into a cancer battle alone if you want a chance of winning. At my side was a legion of people who've earned my everlasting gratitude.

On the medical front: leading the team in Houston: Dr. Eric Bernicker, outstanding oncologist and human being. His RNs took excellent care of me. Thank you to Grathem, Janan, Kathy and Karen. The surgeons at St. Luke's who wielded their scalpels and machinery with great care and precision, granting me another chance at life. Thank you seems insignificant. So, THANK YOU.

Dr. Susan Minton, in Tampa. Another outstanding practitioner of cancer care. I got lucky when I found her.

Dr. Barbara Edelman, who confirmed my choice of lumpectomy with her research into health care outcomes. Thanks, cuz.

Dr. Melvin Pratter, Professor of Medicine and close friend. He confirmed my choice, too, after I made it.

On the personal front:

I'd be nowhere without my friends. Whether in town or a thousand miles away, their presence in my life matters tremendously.

Teddy and Richie Grossman, your weekly calls kept me going at the worst of times. I counted on Margo Pratter's sweet friendship across a thousand miles. Phyllis and Jeff Schneider, thank you for loving Mike and me through all the bad times. Kate Lyons, you made every workday a pleasure and lifted my concerns about the students while Craig Rench knew how to listen. He had no choice—he was surrounded by a couple of talkative females.

Pat O'Dea Rosen, I will never forget our Wednesday lunches and how you kept me sane by talking about writing. Pat Kay, another Houston Writing Buddy who kept up with me online and in person.

And to my grown-up boys: Andrew, David and Rick – a mom couldn't have picked three finer men than you as sons. If I wore a vest, my buttons would pop. I love you all.

RESOURCES/BIBLIOGRAPHY

Nonprofit Foundations

Facing Our Risk Of Cancer Empowered (F.O.R.C.E.) www.facingourrisk.org

No Surrender Breast Cancer Foundation http://nosurrenderbreastcancerhelp.org

Susan G. Komen for the Cure http://ww5.komen.org/

American Cancer Society http://www.cancer.org/

For Reference

Confronting Hereditary Breast and Ovarian Cancer: Identify Your Risk, Understand Your Options, Change Your Destiny by Sue Friedman, Rebecca Sutphen, Kathy Steligo (The Johns Hopkins University Press 2012)

Books of Interest (real women, real stories mentioned in HOPEFULLY EVER AFTER: Breast Cancer, Life and Me)

Bald in the Land of Big Hair: A True Story by Joni Rogers (Harper Perennial 2002)

UPLIFT: Secrets from the Sisterhood of Breast Cancer Survivors by Barbara Delinsky (Atria 2001)

First, You Cry: The Classic, Inspiring Story of One Woman's Triumph Over Breast Cancer by Betty Rollins (Lippincott 1976, Harper Perennial 2000)

The Middle Place by Kelly Corrigan (Hyperion Voice 2008)

This book is not intended as a substitute for the medical advice of physicians. The reader should regularly consult a physician in matters relating to his/her health and particularly with respect to any symptoms that may require diagnosis or medical attention.

I have tried to recreate events, locales and conversations from my memories of them. Some names and identifying details have been changed to protect the privacy of individuals.

Read an excerpt from Linda's current novel, *FAMILY INTERRUPTED*, available for eReaders and in-print.

Chapter One

CLAIRE BARNES

Houston, Texas
September

"*Bellisima! Brava!* Your best work yet, Signora Barnes. Maybe you give Leonardo some competition?"

I rolled my eyes and grinned at my instructor. "Leonardo can rest easy."

Dr. Colombo teased, exhorted, or flirted with his students on a regular basis, especially the talented ones, but comparing my work to the *Mona Lisa* was going too far, even for this powerhouse.

I stepped away from my easel and focused on a portrait of a young girl peeking sideways under half-closed lids. I'd called it *Girl with Secrets*. The child held secrets I wanted to know.

"Your daughter, yes?" Colombo asked, his voice a deep rumble.

DNA didn't lie. I nodded and said, "On the outside, Kayla's mine, brown eyes and blonde hair, but inside, she's her dad, an unquenchable extrovert. Sometimes my daughter's surrounded by more friends than my house can hold." My pride in Kayla overrode the mock complaint. "She's twelve-and-a-half, almost a teenager—almost grown up, as she likes to remind me."

"Ahh." He sighed as if he understood. "I have two daughters, Signora, and I know how they too much wanted to be women but were not ready, *never* ready in the eyes of their mama."

The man had nailed it, nailed my heart. I wasn't ready for Kayla to grow up and fly away, especially with her brother applying for college this year. I wasn't ready to let either of my children go.

"This portrait of your daughter.... It is...is..." Colombo waved his arm this way and that as he searched his English vocabulary. "Exceptional!" His voice rang out, eyes shone. The young student at the next easel walked over and stared.

"Holy Toledo, Claire," she whispered. "Your kid could step right into the room. How'd you do that?"

Surprised and uncomfortable—I was just a student like the others—I wondered how to respond. Capturing Kayla's image had come easily. I knew every smile, nuance, and angle of her face. I knew how she looked when she was happy or sad or puzzled. The work hadn't been *that* difficult to execute.

"I'm her mom," I finally said as if that explained everything. To me, it did. A few of the students nodded. Others seemed to be waiting for more, which I guess was not surprising. I was old enough to be their moms!

"I know all Kayla's moods and expressions," I said. "I can picture her rolling her eyes at her dad's bad jokes.

And I've seen those dark eyes shine when he walks through the door each night."

My classmates seemed glued to my words, so on I went. "And her hair...it's so thick and long, she still needs my help combing it after a shampoo." I thought about how I could never resist kissing her neck and laughing when she groaned, "Ooh, Mom."

Pointing to Kayla's hair in the painting, I said, "See the rich auburn color here? In the summer sun, it glows like a banked fire. Maybe next time, I'll paint her outdoors."

I finally shut up, and in the quiet room, I felt the other students' eyes on me and forced myself not to squirm. Being the center of attention was Jack's specialty, not mine.

"Don't be too impressed," I quickly added. "I've sketched her hundreds of times. Maybe thousands." I was trying to be modest for the sake of my classmates, but dang, I found it hard not to celebrate. *See, Jack? I told you I had talent! And the validation feels damn good.*

My endless drawings through the years had meant less to him than the bottom line of our construction company. But when I turned forty-five last year, I knew I couldn't keep waiting for Jack's promise of "one day." I'd seized my own moment and enrolled in the University of Houston's MFA program.

I was a second-year student now, and whatever artistic gifts I possessed were being revealed under the guidance of a marvelous staff. No instructor, however, could match the gusto and intuition of Professor Colombo. Like the original explorer, this Colombo also led his crew on a voyage of discovery. *Create like Michelangelo! Find the heart, the soul of the stone, and chip away the rest. Fall in love with your subject, and it will show.*

The teacher had a point. I certainly loved *my* subject.

"So, Signora, we will spotlight *Girl with Secrets* in the *galleria* next month, at the exhibition."

I pivoted toward the man so sharply I almost tripped. "Exhibit? But I'm not ready." Was I? Sure I was living my dream, learning and improving, but didn't I need more experience and confidence before showing my work in public? If I'd spent the past twenty years painting instead of decorating model homes for Barnes Construction, I would have been more than willing to exhibit.

"With respect, Signora Barnes, you do not decide who is ready." Colombo swept away my protest with no hesitation. "I, myself, handpicked the twelve artists in this class. I studied the portfolios from last year. You are more than good enough. Art is to be shared and enjoyed. To touch the soul. Claire—or Clara, I may call you Clara? Good. Let me tell you something else, a secret between us."

He glanced around the room while I stood alert, heart racing at being the focus of his pointed attention. Handpicked for his class? I'd had no idea. When he turned to me again, his gaze holding mine, a frisson of electricity danced down my back. His index finger covered his mouth for a moment, reminding me that this was a private conversation.

"You are my most promising student in a long time," he began. "Your hands transform what your heart feels and your eyes see." He tapped his chest. "The emotions here, inside, are on the canvas too! Do you think everyone can do that?"

I took the question seriously. "Well, not the man on the street, but the other students...?"

"You are not listening, Clara! Am I speaking with the 'other students'?"

As his words began to sink in, my excitement soared. My attention focused exclusively on Colombo, and my classmates seemed to disappear, leaving the professor and me in our own private world. The man was implying I was extra special, wasn't he? Oh, Lordy, I hoped so. And then I'd tell Jack. And maybe we could hire a decorator, someone to replace me at work. If that happened, I could finally devote more of my time to art and less to business. Could the day get any better?

"Thank you. Thank you." I'd finally found my voice. "I appreciate everything you've said and done. I know I've improved as an artist because of you." *Take a breath. Calm down.* I turned my attention back to my painting of Kayla. Despite all the compliments, evaluating my own stuff was difficult, especially at this professional level. Sometimes I was too critical, sometimes too soft.

"All right, Professor. I'll agree with you. It's pretty good."

"Very good, Clara. Excellent."

During the past month, I'd started trusting Colombo's judgment despite him being a showman. His own work had impressed me—his use of light and shadow in particular—and the Art Department had been delighted to attract this visiting professor. Now I felt lucky to be studying with him. Even privileged. I knew my talented classmates felt the same. But to be called his best student in a long time?

I scanned the room for glimpses of the others' work and realized my fellow students had already put away their easels and were leaving the studio.

Quickly checking the wall clock, I felt my stomach tighten. "Oh, God, I'll be late. And Kayla has a dental appointment." Forgetting about my schedule and kids was unlike me. Had I encouraged the professor's compliments? Our lingering after class?

Pushing those thoughts aside, I quickly became a focused mom again. I carried Kayla's portrait to my private studio space, threw my smock on a chair, and shouted a goodbye to the professor while running toward the staircase. Down, down, down, until I exited the building to the parking lot, digging for my car keys at the same time. Finally, I thrust myself into the driver's seat and revved the engine. Back to reality. Back to Jack, the kids, my domestic life, and my working life. Tomorrow was soon enough to face Colombo and his compliments. A handsome Colombo with his dark mane of hair touched by wings of silver. I wondered how many art students, both in Italy and America, had produced his portrait while studying with him. My fingers reached for a phantom pencil.

#

I followed the restrained campus speed limit but hit the gas as soon as I reached the interstate. Twenty-four miles stood between the University of Houston and home. I gave myself fifteen minutes. The miles disappeared until sirens blared and lights flashed in my rearview mirror. Damn, damn, damn. I slowed down, pulled over, and prepared to smile my widest. Jack always said my smile was my secret weapon. I didn't necessarily agree but was prepared to give it a try if it meant getting Kayla to her appointment on time.

I rolled down my window and beamed.

"License and registration, ma'am." No twinkle, no smile, no sense of humor. Pure cop face.

I handed over the documents and used my cell as I waited for Houston's Finest to check out my identity. I had to leave a message at the house but wasn't really surprised. If Ian had to watch his sister, he'd be sure they shot hoops in the driveway or kicked a soccer ball on the lawn. God forbid he'd set a good example by doing homework right away. So irresponsible. I sighed a frustrated sigh. A mother's sigh.

"Ma'am, you were clocked doing eighty in a sixty. That's twenty miles over the limit."

I could do the math. "Any chance of turning this into a warning? I'm usually excellent at following the rules." *Smile.*No answer except for the scratching of his pen. Five minutes later, I was on my way with a ticket nearing two hundred dollars and an invitation to driving school. For the rest of the trip, I crept at posted speeds until, with a sigh of relief, I finally entered my subdivision and turned left around the lake toward Bluebonnet Drive.

As I approached, I saw a small crowd milling on the corner, blocking my street. In the mid-distance was a revolving red glow. My body tensed, every muscle taut with strain at the possibilities. I lowered my window when I saw my friend Anne Conroy waving at me.

"She's here," Anne called over her shoulder while rushing toward my vehicle. "Pull over. You need to park right now."

I didn't like how she looked. My hands began to tingle, but I followed her directions.

"There's been an accident, Claire."

"What? Who?"

Instead of answering, Anne opened my door and pulled me out. "It's Kayla. She was hit by a car. The EMTs are lifting her into the ambulance right now."

My worst fear.... I took off like a track star. A path opened as I headed for the gurney. Around me were familiar faces I could barely recognize because I saw only one face. Kayla. My beautiful Kayla, lying on that narrow bed, her complexion snow-white, forehead swollen, head enlarged, and blood oozing from her ears. Her stillness frightened me most.

"I'm here, baby-girl. Mama's right here." I leaned over her and kissed her cool cheek. No response.

"Ma'am, we've got to get her in the truck."

One medic spoke to me while the other was arranging stuff—tubes, IVs, and God-knows-what. They hoisted the gurney, and I jumped in beside it while scanning the crowd for Ian. Where was that boy? Then I saw him, right in front of me, sobbing aloud with tears running thick down his face.

"I'm sorry, I'm sorry, but we were only throwing a football," he cried, his voice cracking. "That's all...."

"You should have been doing homework," I snapped.

He ignored me and pointed at a young woman sitting on the ground, a stranger. "She was driving and...and..."

Glancing at her, I took a mental snapshot, certain I'd recall the details later. I didn't care about the driver then. Instead, anger, fear, and dread filled me, and I lashed out. "How could you have let this happen? You were in charge."

"But it wasn't my fault! I've told you a million times I'm not a babysitter. Maybe if you were home more, Kayla would be okay. It wasn't my...fault."

Because it's my fault. My fault for being late. That was the bottom line. My son and I were at odds again, and remorse filled me. "I'm so sorry, Ian," I whispered. "It's all right. You'll be okay. Kayla will too." *She had to be.* "Hang out with Anne and Maddy for awhile, and I'll see you tonight."

"Gotta close these doors, ma'am," said the EMT, suiting action to his words.

For a moment, I worried about leaving Ian but later was glad I did. My son didn't need to witness or hear the conversations that followed.

#

Kayla lingered for five days. Jack and I slept at the hospital, neither of us wanting to leave. We drank strong tea, wrapped ourselves in warm blankets, and had quiet conversations with the staff.

When I mentioned to Jack how kind the nurses were, he shrugged and stepped closer to Kayla's bed. "It's part of their job." His words were abrupt, curt, and cold, a rarity for my husband.

"But only kind hearts become nurses in the first place," I argued, as if making my point would make everything better. It made nothing better.

Six weeks had passed since Kayla died, but I still remembered the name of every medic on the unit. I still pictured the IV bags with their liquids dripping into Kayla's arm one drop at a time, the orange chairs Jack and I dozed on, and the plantings between the parking lot and Kayla's hospital wing. Most of all, I remembered holding Kayla's hand, stroking her cheek, and talking, talking, talking, praying she'd hear my voice and smile. I remembered that insulated hospital world in detail.

But I couldn't remember my daughter's funeral.

Vague recollections of friends and family surrounding us at the service were all that stayed with me. I'd watched their mouths move but heard nothing. I'd seen nothing. Usually, I'd notice particulars—the cut of a blouse, a change of hairstyle, a newly framed picture—but my powers of observation disappeared that day. All gone. Just like Kayla.

Friends said that Jack and I had been amazing. What nonsense! We were numb. Paralyzed by the unthinkable. They described Jack catching me as I fainted at the cemetery. I didn't remember falling, but they said I'd collapsed the moment our daughter's casket was lowered into the ground. I believed them. I'd become a zombie, one of the walking dead.

At home, meals arrived, coffee brewed, and the refrigerator and house remained equally full. Our loved ones surrounded us, stayed with us, supported us. My parents. Jack's parents. Their lips trembled and pain etched their faces.

But no one managed to answer the one question that mattered: how could a vibrant twelve-year-old kick a soccer ball one day and lie in a coma the next? The question haunted me still. I knew there were reasons. Cause-and-effect type reasons. But I hadn't been able to accept them. How would I ever cope with this nightmare? The memories...the memories...

When Kayla was five years old, she'd said, "Mama, if you turn the number eight on its side, you know what you get?"

"What?"

"Infinity!"

A grown-up word. She'd giggled, eyes beaming, so proud of herself for surprising me. I hadn't known how she'd come up with the word, but I'd been pretty sure her brother had some influence there. *Infinity*. An appropriate description for the days that now came and went, unremarkable one from the other, simply periods of light and dark I sometimes noticed through the windows of my diminished home.

So, six weeks later, I was still a mess. Jack too. Not sure about Ian. He'd been hanging out with his friends almost twenty-four/seven. Maybe if I started cooking—really cooking—again every day, he'd find his way home for dinner. He loved meatballs and spaghetti. Heck, he used to love anything I'd put on the table. A growing boy needed nourishment, and we all used to laugh about our skinny boy devouring more than his dad. He'd filled out some this year.

Jack finally returned to work yesterday because

he'd been afraid to leave me alone sooner. He'd taken calls at the house after the first two weeks and depended on his staff to keep Barnes Construction going. He had great employees, but we all knew that my Cracker Jack was the engine driving the company. It was his baby, his creation, and certainly his success. I sensed he was anxious to get back to work full-time while I, on the other hand, had no heart for anything, not even painting.

Thirty minutes after Jack left, the doorbell rang. I sure didn't want any company, so I peeped through the sidelight curtain, ready to ignore any social caller. But I couldn't ignore a FedEx delivery. Occasionally, items for Barnes Construction were shipped to the house. This item was a pretty large box, which the driver pushed over the threshold for me.

Return address: University of Houston, Art Department. I hadn't stepped onto the campus since that horrible day. I hadn't contacted the department or the registrar to officially drop out of school. Maybe they wanted clarification. I opened the outside envelope and extracted a note:

Whenever you are ready, Clara, come back. I am keeping your last painting here. You have much art still to make, and I am saving your place. CC.

The man would have a long wait. None of it mattered anymore. Only Kayla mattered. I didn't open the box, didn't look at any of my portfolio items. Instead, I dragged the carton into the guest room and closed the door. I brushed my hands together and walked to the kitchen. My college adventure was over. Maybe someday, I'd have the courage to retrieve *Girl with Secrets*.

I spent the rest of the morning alone, looking through photo albums, torturing myself. Jack called me every hour.

"How're you doing?" he asked.

How did he think I was doing? "Fine."

But of course, I'd never be fine again.

After four phone calls, I threatened to ignore his number on the Caller ID. We finally compromised. He'd stop phoning if I promised to take a walk. He said I hadn't gone out of the house since the funeral. Somehow, I also promised to track Ian down, cook a real dinner, and then make love to Jack that night. I promised a lot of things because when you lived in a time warp, nothing mattered. Not even promises made.

As it turned out, however, I did take a walk in the afternoon. Maybe the milder temperatures and gentler sun lured me, or maybe it was the general quiet with everyone else at work or school. I thought a solitary walk would be a perfect first venture outside. Unfortunately, one of my neighbors spotted me, a neighbor I didn't know well, and I wanted to retreat but couldn't.

"I'm so sorry, Mrs. Barnes...Claire," she said, full of sympathy.

I just nodded. A tiny nod. I pressed my lips together and began to stride past her.

"Sometimes," she continued, "it's hard to accept God's will."

I jerked to a full stop. My heart pounded, my vision blurred. God's will? God's will? I screamed silently. What had my innocent child done to deserve this fate? I whirled and stared at the woman for what seemed hours. Her self-righteousness oozed like the slow-running sap of a sugar maple tree. My palm itched. My fingers curled. Her cheek would make a good target. *Don't do it, Claire! Don't do it....* But I was in my time warp, watching myself from afar as I lifted my arm and smacked her across the face.

"That was God's will too," I said and walked off, confirming I was a long way from acceptance. If there was such a thing.

#

When Jack arrived from work, a home-cooked meal waited for him. Ian sat at the table too, thanks to my meatball bribe. The men ate with gusto. I managed one bite to ten of theirs and hoped Jack wouldn't notice. When their first hunger pangs had been satisfied, I announced, "I might go to jail."

Ian's mouth made a perfect O.

"You might what?" asked Jack. But when he heard the story of my walk, his blue eyes glowed, and his grin stretched across his face. Then he swung me around, laughed, and cried. "I couldn't survive without *both* my girls, and you're coming to life again. I love you so much, Claire. We'll get through this. Somehow, we'll get through." Then he looked at me with his I-have-a-great-idea expression.

"It's been more than a month, Claire. How about coming back to work? The company needs you. More importantly, *I* need you. You know how the economy sucks, and I might have overreached, but we've contracted to build in the Eagle Ranch subdivision. We've got four brand-new models for you to work your magic on."

I felt myself shrivel. Jack depended on me to dress up our models to their best advantage. I supposed I could manage the decorating part, but interacting with all the people involved in the business? Making intelligent conversation with Realtors, decorators, home buyers, vendors, and municipal departments was beyond me. I couldn't focus for more than ten seconds on anything but the family photo albums I'd browsed through that day. I couldn't fathom how Jack managed to handle his responsibilities.

"Sorry," I said, shaking my head. "I'm not ready." When I saw his disappointment, I added, "But I am ready to keep my promise about this." I snaked my arms around his neck, tugged him toward me, and tilted my head back. His eyes brightened again, and our kiss sizzled at first contact.

"Yuck. I am so outta here." Ian grabbed his backpack and left the room, calling, "I'll be at Danny's."

"The kid has great instincts," mumbled Jack, his lips on mine again.

I wanted this raw encounter with Jack. I'd been thinking about it on and off all day, knowing I needed it more now than when I was twenty-one. I didn't know why. Didn't care about the reason. Not then, anyway. I just wanted the numbness to go away, if only for a few minutes.

Interlocked, we headed toward our bedroom, automatically kicking the door shut before pulling at our clothes. I was desperate to be skin-to-skin, touching, rubbing, stroking. Feeling! Feeling Jack's muscles move under my fingers. Borrowing his warmth, his strength. He knew my hot spots...just where, just how.... I knew his, too...just where, just how....

We twined closely around each other on the bed, our limbs weaving like yarn on a loom enveloping each other, so in synch, so frantic that soon there was no rhythm at all. And then, and then...oh, God...approaching that point of no return...vibrating through shimmering reds, scarlet and crimson, heading toward the neons, gold and hot orange...until the sun shattered, and we shattered. Together.

Our first communion since Kayla died.

I burst into tears.

Jack was still trying to catch his breath, but he reached out and coaxed me against him, across his chest. A very familiar position. "Aww, Claire. Don't cry.

You're all right. You're all right."

No, I wasn't. "I shouldn't feel this good. Kayla—" But I hadn't thought about my daughter for the past ten minutes. Had it taken the most basic of human instincts to break through my grief? As though in punishment, a new wave of grief surged through me. *I'm sorry, sweetheart.*

"We can't bring her back," Jack whispered. "But it seems that you and I are still alive." He spoke slowly, emphasizing each word. "In fact, we're very much alive. That was good, Claire. And healthy for us. So keep it on your to-do list, will ya?"

I couldn't blame him for wanting to reclaim as much normalcy as possible in our abnormal world, and intimacy had always been a healthy part of our marriage. However, my tears kept dribbling onto Jack's chest.

"If you keep on crying, my love, then I will too. And we'll both go back to being zombies like in the beginning."

"I still feel like one," I said between sobs. "I think I always will."

"No, no. I don't think it works like that. It's not forever. But in the meantime, I like having a naked zombie in my arms."

Jabbing him, I said, "No jokes."

"I'm just trying to—"

"I know, Jack. I know. You're trying to pretend we're okay."

"What's wrong with pretending for awhile if it works? I have to believe we'll get there someday, that we'll be strong again someday."

Granted, my numbness had disappeared during our sexual encounter as I'd suspected it would. But I didn't believe Jack and I would ever be strong again. I didn't care about "someday," a nebulous time in a hazy future. My heart was breaking now.

Another new story by Linda Barrett is available now! For holiday fun, read an excerpt from CELEBRATE! This heartwarming anthology from On Fire Fiction includes works by Barbara McMahon, Deb Salonen, Karen Sandler, Rogenna Brewer and

Linda Barrett's MAN OF THE HOUSE

Linda's celebrating Mother's Day, Father's Day and second chances at love.

NANCY WYATT

   This can't be good news. The readout on Nancy Wyatt's desk phone said Pulitzer Middle School, Hillsboro FL, and her stomach knotted as tightly as a fishing line around bait. Bobby was either sick or in trouble. Please, God, no more incidents. She took a breath and picked up the receiver.

Five minutes later she threw herself behind the wheel of her trusty old Honda, and headed toward trouble. She'd be taking Bobby back to work with her. Fighting required a two day suspension. Fighting! Bobby had always been a good kid. A sweet boy. As an only child, he'd had no one to fight with!

Nancy's fingers tapped the wheel, her thoughts in turmoil. Did young boys morph into strangers when they hit their teen years? Why hadn't she seen the change? They'd become so close, she and her son, a team of two who'd clung to each other after losing Jason four years ago. She sighed from deep within her soul, a long, mournful sound. Jason had been a wonderful husband, a terrific dad. She could still picture her two guys having a catch with each other in their back yard. Baseball had become Bobby's passion by then.

Even at nine years old, he'd shown promise with a good eye and a good arm. And now he was the starting pitcher for his Little League team. Since Jason's death, Nancy had tried to be strong for her son, cheering and supportive. She'd thought she'd succeeded. But maybe not.

She pulled into the visitors' parking lot and made her way to the principal's office. Good God, the principal's office! As a kid, she'd never been sent there. She supposed she'd been a goody, goody kind of girl. Cooperative, studious—definitely not a trouble maker. And yet, this principal's office had become too familiar since the spring semester had started. Middle School years were expected to be the roughest, but…Bobby?

Or maybe his issues weren't about school. His grades hadn't faltered, so maybe something else was at play. Maybe Steve? Maybe Bobby's attitude change

LINDA BARRETT

coincided with Steve Duggan coming into their lives. The thought resonated and hit her with the force of a fast pitch. Later. She'd think about it later.

Nancy spotted her son through the plate glass window of the general office. He slouched on a bench, staring at the door. Not blinking. Just waiting. Waiting for his mom and whatever happened next. His hair needed cutting. The hanks falling onto his forehead, however, couldn't hide the swelling or reddish-purple hue now blooming around his eye. His hair couldn't hide the blood oozing from scratches along his cheek. This boy was not the Bobby she knew or thought she knew so well. Where was the son she'd raised?

She rushed into the room. "Bobby! What happened?"

His mouth twisted. "Nothin'."

"Nothing? Come on, sweetie. Have you looked in the mirror?"

"Ask him." Bobby's chin jutted toward the principal's private door. "He thinks he knows everything."

She looked over to see the principal coming toward her, followed by a boy about Bobby's age. A boy sporting wounds similar to Bobby's. A boy she recognized, one of the students she tutored at the learning center where she worked evenings to supplement her part-time librarian's salary.

"Phillip?"

The boy nodded.

"They're both suspended for two days," said Mr. Emanuel. "Fighting will not be tolerated here, and neither of them had anything to say."

Phillip sat down at the other end of the bench. The boys knew each other only through school. They might have seen each other at the learning center a few times when she'd had to bring her son, but they weren't fast friends. They had no history. What could have set them off?

"That's not true." Bobby got to his feet and looked at the principal. "I had something to say. I said that he started it."

The principal motioned Nancy and Bobby inside his office. "And last week, you said Nathan Brownstein started it. The month before, it was....let's see." He scanned the computer screen. "It was John Pappas."

She recognized the names from her prior visits to this office. But now, with Phillip added to the list, she made the connection.

"I tutor all those boys after school," she said. "So Bobby, what's this about? You don't take any courses at the learning center. You barely know these kids."

Her son jumped to his feet. "I know enough. And I wish you didn't teach there."

#

BOBBY

My mom doesn't understand anything. Especially about guys. She thinks that Phillip and the others really care about pulling their grades up. They don't give a flying you-know-what about their grades. I'd use the F-bomb but that would make me as gross as those jerks. No better than guys I'll have to keep beating up if they call my mom a MILF one more time.

I bet she doesn't even know what that means. My mother is very pretty, real-ly pretty, and she doesn't even know it. But they know it. That's what guys my age do. They look at girls...and women...and maybe they look harder at a woman without a husband. Well, they'd better stop staring at her. And Steve Duggan had better stop, too. He's been hanging around Mom for the last few months, and I think she likes him! The whole thing gives me a stomach ache. And I don't get bad stomach aches anymore, not since after Dad died.

I guess I haven't been afraid of anything much since I passed my thirteenth birthday last year and stopped being a kid. Personally, I think thirteen is where the line is drawn. On one side, you're just a boy. Step over it, and you're a man. As soon as I hit thirteen, I looked at my little family—Mom and me—and realized I was the "man" of the house. The idea felt comfortable. I felt comfortable. It seemed right.

But as soon as Mom introduced me to Steve Duggan, my comfortable world shifted. I thought the earth jumped right off its axis. When I looked into Duggan's face on that first day, I knew I was looking at trouble. It wasn't because he was big—heck, some of my coaches are bigger--or because he had these gray eyes that gleamed like the sun shining off metal, or because those eyes stared right at me, maybe even through me. His strong handshake didn't scare me either. Not then. I could have handled all those things easily, except for one small hitch: my mom.

The person who scared me most on that first day was my own mother. And that's how I knew Steve Duggan spelled trouble.

Printed by Amazon Italia Logistica S.r.l.
Torrazza Piemonte (TO), Italy

33549627R00116